PRAISE FOR THE NIHILIST'S POCKET SURVIVAL GUIDE TO MODERN SOCIETY

TUNGYN CHEQUE

THE NIHILIST'S POCKET SURVIVAL GUIDE TO MODERN SOCIETY

TUNGYN CHEQUE

VOX VERITAS VITA

PRESS

Library of Congress Control Number: 2023921439

ISBN: 979-8-218-31900-7 (Paperback)

ISBN: 979-8-218-31901-4 (Ebook)

For all those who appreciate the spirited dance of serious and silly

CONTENTS

CAUTION

Don't say I didn't warn you

WARNING: The content herein is dangerous and may cause harm or permanent injury to your mind. Enter at your own risk. Proceed with caution...*

*In case of accidental overdose, do not call your physician and waste precious time; instead, contact poison control at the National Institutes of Mental Health (or smoke, imbibe, or consume something mildly intoxicating and continue reading)... God Save the Queen.

ORIGINS

How do you repay a kindness?

R. L.—no middle name; hence, no middle initial—was born and bred a nihilist. Accounting for the breeding part were a ditzy mother, with a brain ravaged by too many dubious drugs in her youth, and a disillusioned father, worn down and out by a failed society, not quite Willie Loman, but still a defeated shell of a man, prone to following in grandfather's over-imbibing but not abusive ways. Nevertheless, he maintained a healthy opinion of himself despite life's burdens, and notwithstanding a paucity of other people who shared his self-inflated opinion. Perhaps this demonstrates the value of self-esteem. R. L. had chosen not to follow in his father's footsteps and instead chose a different path, the path less followed. And this has made all the difference.

To be exact, R. L. had not been a nihilist his whole life; a few hours must be subtracted. The birth of his nihilist identity stretched not to his actual birth by Caesarian after a fruitless Lamaze-style attempt while immersed in a pool of water failed to coax him through the birth canal. His nihilist self was born shortly thereafter, with his name, or at least what was recorded on his birth certificate—Rectum Leviticus. Now some might pause at this curious first and last name, not even proper for a sobriquet. In fact, his name came from deference to an act of kindness imparted by a stranger, not that his parents relied upon the kindness of strangers in a Blanche Dubois sort of way, so much as in recognition of the divine providence of a preacher.

The story of origin, his personal narrative given in explanation, but not apology, by his parents—his father, actually—went something along the lines of: "We had been hitchhiking in Northern California after a concert two weeks or so before your mother delivered. This fellow with burning eyes in an old pickup truck gave us a lift. He saw your mom was in a child-bearing time of her life and must have felt sorry for us. His first name was Joshua and his last name—can you believe it?—was Leviticus, same as your grandfather who endowed me with the family inheritance. A name is a powerful thing, son."

The condensed version of the rest of that story had to do with grandpa, who R. L. had never met, hailing from Bible belting country and being none too pleased with mom and dad's wayfaring hippie, free love, drug culture ways and more or less disowning them. The parts about his drinking and wife beating didn't usually get told without the disclaimer, "But he always went to church on Sundays." Nevertheless, Joshua with same last name, but not likely a relative, seemed to have made quite the impression on M and P. He was Rector for some kind of worship community, but this being Northern California in the 80's, could have been the progenitor of the Church of the Flying Spaghetti Monster for all R. L. knew.

As his mother told it, "I began to go into labor, and Rector Leviticus drove an extra fifty miles to get me to the hospital. Even though it turned out to be false labor, you know those Braxton Hickey kinds of cramps, your father and I were determined to repay his kindness."

Invariably they would both chime in together at this point, "It's not our fault they misspelled it on the birth certificate."

Growing up, other kids would make fun of his name. At first it bothered R. L., and the insults continued. Then he realized he didn't care, but this was not pretend not-caring—it was the real deal. When he stopped caring, the taunting stopped too. This amounted to a formative and pivotal moment, an epiphany of sorts about the effectiveness of not caring as a strategy to address life in general. The true epiphany came later in life with the recognition that names in general shouldn't be a big deal at all. In other words, no one should care much about a silly name, least of all himself.

What's in a name anyway? Would not a rose with a different name still smell as sweet? Would not flatus still smell as foul? How would a flower named "fart" smell? It seemed to R. L. that questions of this import had more bearing and were immanently more important than his name. He could be named Walter after his father, but surely this should not change the character of the man that R. L. had grown to become. Unless of course he followed the trajectory of the man called "Sue" in the Johnny Cash song. Some things are worth caring for, but his name was not among them. Neither he nor anyone ought to care a flying fig or frig or any other exclamation, vulgar or otherwise, about anyone else's name.

This seminal revelation represented a giant leap in philosophical inquiry about the nature of caring. His list of things to care about got shorter as the years went on. Under a process of steady refinement and distillation he surmised people cared too much about unimportant things. In the zeal of his youthful twenties, he contemplated starting a movement to call attention to the need for less caring, until he realized, in startling enlightenment, that no one would care about his movement. And so, in the space of time it took to consume two large mugs of dark beer, he went from founding his movement to becoming the first and only martyr to sacrifice himself for the cause by paradoxically abandoning the cause. Reaching this enlightened conclusion and making the ultimate sacrifice, thereby quashing his zeal by demonstrating the importance about not caring for foolish things such as the movement he founded, coincided precisely with the final gulp and a satisfied wipe of foam from his lips. Henceforth, his list of things utterly worth caring about remained short. This unburdened him to enjoy a surprising degree of freedom.

Fast-forward: R. L. is thirty something, living in a run-down Brooklyn apartment that in his parents' day would be called a tenement, which was a better word than his grandparents would have used––the projects, which was just a sugarcoated word for slum. There you have it. He lived in a slum. But this was not because he was not educated, and not because he was not gainfully employed. Indeed, he had the requisite paper from, in his particular circumstance, a not well-known or overly reputable liberal arts college in the Midwest. This choice was made after realistically evaluating his limited financial resources, inauspicious grades and SAT performance, alternatives to not pursuing a vaunted college education, and wanting to get the hell out of New York, at least for a spell. And, this said nothing about his underlying intelligence, IQ, EQ, propensity to challenge authority, which had miraculously only landed him in jail twice, or general refusal to engage the hamster wheel of modern debt-plagued life encumbering so many of his contemporaries.

He did have a meaningless Bachelor's degree, meaningless because it said nothing about the quality or substance of his collegiate educational experience, but did theoretically give him a leg up in the competitive job market of modern times while encumbering him with only a modest $20,000.00 of debt, and seemingly distinguishing him as marginally superior among his fellow drones at XYZ, his current place of gainful employment that he had somehow managed to have for three years while accruing only a single, measly, almost insignificant reprimand. Such reprimand derived from a mere dress code violation, a pittance slap-on-the wrist that nevertheless gave his employer just means to deny a salary raise due to performance issues in his HR file. Whatever.

As to his abode, it represented nothing fancy, but what would you expect on his salary with his level of debt, his education and job skills, and his freedom from illusory importance? He had all he needed for an urban existence. It was less than palatial, nor exactly envisioned in the great American dream of a single-family dwelling in suburbia with an SUV and a late-model sedan parked in a two-car garage, adorned with bumper-stickers extolling their children's inconsequential accomplishments, with a nicely manicured lawn tended to by the prideful owner of an oversized John Deere tractor mower not necessary to care for a 40 X 40 sized postage patch of grass, but fully demonstrating the economic success of the inhabitants dwelling within while camouflaging the ridiculous mortgage payments, car payments, and tractor payments heaped upon student debt payments for said inhabitants, who both laud similar paper work from degree-granting nondescript institutions of higher learning. Not his dream, despite its pervasiveness. He refused to run in that hamster wheel. Quite possibly, that qualified him as a dangerous insurrectionist.

No, R. L. lived a somewhat different version of the same American dream, not the H. P. Lovecraft equivalent of an Orwellian nightmare of corporations screwing their workforce under the watchful eye of Uncle Sam screwing the citizenry under the auspices of Democracy. Nevertheless, he was not an anarchist. He left that ultra-libertarian nonsense extremism to his dear friend Blythe, and her ilk, a stable of like-minded seditionist anti-statists who had no tolerance for rules or restrictions.

Nah, he didn't subscribe to that sort of crap. He saw what was going on, like some latter-day Alexis de Tocqueville chronicling what the status quo across the pond in America is doing. Through careful observation, he had picked up bits and pieces, patch-worked them together and had managed to figure out a thing or two. Shit happening in Europe was pretty much the same *merde* happening here.

He had managed to survive in a Brooklyn slum, a ratty shit hole of a place or a shitty rat hole of a place depending on what particular side of his used mattress from Goodwill he happened to wake up on that day. Kind of like a Turkish Kurd is similar to a Kurdish Turk depending on what rebel force from what nationalistic territory you are from. Same shit happening there too, just different people pulling the strings and holding the guns, but not all that very different when he stopped to think about it. And when he did think about it, the canvas portraying the state of the world showed a picture of things being pretty messed up. He knew it. The towering Western worldwide Roman Empire, an imperialistic death-star of power, was crumbling, rotting or collapsing under its own weight due to the flimsy near-vacuum upon which it was built and operated. He knew it, but still he managed to survive, not as a matter of ingenuity or optimism or hard work and dedication. The never ending litany of mumbo jumbo pseudo psychology, law of attraction, master of your own fate, goal is to thrive not just survive, providing hope for a better life in exchange for a generous payment to share in these insightful survival tools represented little more than a heapin' smokin' pile of nonsense. R. L. had managed to figure out something that eluded most of his contemporaries. He survived because he just didn't care.

This was not some mega-apathy-indifference kind of not caring, born of suppression and oppression, an apathy whose genesis lay in repeatedly being shocked by unseen scientists as he reached for food or dutifully ran a maze only to be shot down, or more aptly shocked down, until he was little more than a helpless, hapless fur ball of disempowered trembling indifference. Nope. He just didn't care. His nihilism, refined from past to present, gave him the ultimate survival playbook.

That pretty much sums it up: the formation of a nihilist, Rectum Leviticus—college grad, Brooklyn tenement denizen, and social commentator. You would think he would have gotten his name changed or used a nickname, but that would not be in keeping with his nihilistic roots. Born and bred a nihilist—philosophically, ontologically, and existentially—R. L. didn't care about his name, his social status, his job, or his possessions in the way most people do. He got through each day, one at a time, relatively free and unburdened, because when you don't care, stuff doesn't bother you. He survives. This is how he does it:

Rectum's survival Tips, Part One

- *If life deals you a difficult hand, does your mental health improve when you struggle? Don't struggle unless you enjoy suffering. If you enjoy suffering, bamboo shoots under the fingernails might be something to consider.*

- *Not caring is a useful survival skill because when you are not invested in an outcome, you can better tolerate the process. Your first thought in reading this tip should be, "Why should I care?"*

- *Observe around you to look for clues about what is and is not meaningful; however, there is something to be said about going through life completely clueless.*

- *First clue: after your basic needs are met for food, shelter, and elimination, meaning-fulness is rather subjective. If the subjective quality of this statement eludes you, drink or smoke something mildly intoxicating, then re-read chapter one. Repeat until an epiphany occurs.*

WORKING PERSON

What to do when work gives you lemons? Make alphabet soup!

H e had developed a simultaneous great respect and great disdain for the working person in these modern times. Such respect derived from thoughts, not feelings. Given that a basic tenet of nihilistic inclinations is not to imbue emotions, and their attendant attachments, into what really is a rational calculus, he thoughtfully evaluated the circumstances and challenges faced

by society's worker bees and concluded they deserved respect. Yet, worker bees harvest pollen and
tend to the collective needs of the hive society;
in contrast, the modern worker has been duped
into service to some social construct built upon
a foundation of sand, a hallucination of happi-
ness and stature fulfilled by more and more stuff
in a never-ending spiral of unfulfillment. Therein
lay the disdain––not because of those making the
promises of a better life attained by work, but by
the worker dutifully drinking the Kool-Aid con-
cocted and served by the masters of the masses.

Incidentally, he chose the non-sexist, inclusive
term "working person" because he was philosophically opposed to labels such as male, female, trans-
gender that conveniently seem to separate and
fragment and marginalize one particular faction
of humanity against another. And he was particularly opposed, to the point of cringe worthy, when people were relegated to some alphabet soup designation such as, "LGBTQ". We are
people, individuals for sure, but a lettered designation? Seems a bit dehumanizing, but what the hell

would he know, he worked at XYZ Corporation, where he was little more than a number—Employee #1065-228––more than a zip code, but less than a phone number.

XYZ had a suite of offices in a standard office building on the upwards side of downtown. The building certainly had never been nominated, and never would even be remotely considered for an architectural award. It wasn't ghastly; drab and uninspired would be more apt descriptions. White bread, standard issue, garden variety, run-of-the-mill office building—kind of like a standard military issue assault weapon, the kind that had infiltrated the gangs living and working in his slum and all over the country. The assault weapons multiplied like cockroaches or an invasive weed, until they were all over the place. He saw a ten-year old carrying an Uzi, just last week on the playground. "Playground", there's a misnomer, unless you think spraying a batch of your playmates while discharging a high-capacity magazine is fun. To each *his* own, or *her* own, or *their* own.

R. L. decided "it" was the proper pronoun designation for the worker––an "it", an ant, a cog in some immense corporate machinery, much like himself, 1065-228 at XYZ. There is something perfectly clean and neat and sterile putting himself in that context. No one is going to demonstrate, or wear armbands, or ribbons, or take up arms, or lay down in front of a moving tank, or strap a suicide vest on and blow up themselves, and a batch of innocents alongside, while fighting in the name of 1065-228 at XYZ. There is nothing to attach to, get worked up about, or lose sleep over when a human being is reduced to such a metric. That he/she/they might happen to be someone's son, or daughter, or mother, or father, or spouse; whether that PERSON happens to be a talented artist, or writer, or composer, or volunteer, or humanitarian, or thief, villain, or scumbag is irrelevant once they have been reduced to a numeric or alpha-numeric designation. There's a bit of corporate genius in that—having employees that are nothing more than employee numbers. No office parties, retirement send offs, dress down days, girl scout cookie sales, or any personally identifying characteristics to mar or interfere with work, a four-letter word ending in 'k'. That, at least, seemed to be the prevailing mindset of the corporateers who ran XYZ.

The company didn't actually make anything; manufacturing actual products had become anachronistic. Why manufacture when it could all be outsourced to some third-world work force laboring under less than humane conditions, while the negotiators of free trade and globalization collectively turn a blind eye, where a living wage equates to subservience and indentured servitude? At least XYZ did not have constant video surveillance of their workforce drones, and did allow bathroom breaks. Clearly, R. L. and his companion automatons had it good by that standard of comparison.

The company was not clearly in the service industry either, at least if you consider they did not have a customer service line someone could call in order to ask a question or lodge a complaint. That spared the world from having another automated customer non-service line. Spared the world from having to listen to a series of marginally applicable phone options to suffer through and make selections until you could finally be put on hold while listening to nauseating music that, to add insult to injury, is choppy and static-filled, but much worse, provides actual respite from an infinite loop of a cheery-voiced automaton episodically repeating how important your call is. What level of hell from Dante's *Inferno* that derived from he wasn't quite sure. Nope, XYZ had nothing of the sort. They didn't need to. What they did have, not manufacturing and not really servicing anything or anyone, was a B2B business model.

R. L. disliked the alphabet soup of letters and numbers that described so many elements of modern society, things like IBD, and PTSD, and the aforementioned LGBTQ, and a whole variety of other lettered characterizations––NRA, NBA, NSA, OCD, OMG, PBS, PMS, POV––just randomly pulling from the N-O-P section of the alphabet soup. NOPe, didn't like them, but inexplicably, he was not troubled by B2B—Business-to-Business. To be or not to be, that's what it seemed to him B2B was all about. His company was a sort of go-between for other companies, a connector, both an outsourcer and an insourcer, a bit of corporate sorcery when you peel back the curtain and expose the wizard pulling all the levers and pushing all the buttons. XYZ represented some in-between business (much like the hyphen portion of this preceding designation), conducting sleight-of-hand magic, producing profit from upstream and downstream sources, much to the pleasure and delight of investors and shareholders. Fact check: XYZ actually did produce something—profit—much like many other successful corporations conducting their shell game of corporate tactics with the government acting as shill. WTF!

As for Rectum Leviticus, employee #1065-228's role in this grand charade, he, along with many of his fellow cubicons, had the title of "account manager". Exactly what this meant, even R. L. could not say for certain. He read reports, played with numbers, constructed spread-

sheets—work totally superfluous to his college degree and naïve career aspirations, long abandoned
under the reality of reality. Occasionally he went
to meetings, rarely socialized with his fellow office
inmates, and made every effort to ignore his boss,
"Dickhead," to the thirty or so people who worked
with him, among the neatly organized cubicles
arranged within this XYZ location.

This particular group, just a representative sam-
ple, a cohort of fellow worker comrades, he both
loathed and respected. Each and every one of them
managed to slug it out at the soul-sucking work
that XYZ required, neigh demanded, some even
attempting to smile and be upbeat, a noble but
useless endeavor to shine that which could never
be rubbed, polished, or buffed into anything resembling a shine, or even a dull matte. You know,
shit just cannot be worked to a lustrous gloss no
matter how much effort you apply. For this effort,
a "life gives you lemons so let's make some XYZ
lemonade" attitude of "I try and make the best out
of work," R. L. felt respect. Hell, his compatriots
just showing up to work garnered his respect.

But the inverse, the contrary, the opposite opinion was there as well—disdain for the American way, a loathing of sorts that they participated without realizing, oblivious to the truth and justice, or non-justice, of this American way. While he saw it and understood it, and had inured himself to the false belief that this is okay, he could not respect his fellow cubicons that accepted this, bought into this by drinking the Kool-Aid, and were both willing and unwilling participants in this corporate world skullduggery. It was not okay, never had been, and never would be. But "okay" is a judgment, and when the sense of right or wrong, okay or not okay gets violated, that's when people (or even their depersonalized number designations), do crazy things like strap on a suicide vest, or go postal and gun down a batch of their fellow employees in a rage-fueled statement of self-vindication. Usually this included the boss. R. L. himself was undecided on the merits of elimination, other than as applied to bodily function. His boss could go or stay, live or die, 1065-228 didn't much care either way, but he would have more to say about Dickhead as both a subject and object of opinion.

The nihilist felt both a bond of fellowship and solidarity with the XYZ coworkers, while he also begrudgingly felt a bit jealous. They operated in blissful ignorance, managing their accounts, collecting their paychecks, some even aspiring to rise up the corporate ladder. This bliss eluded R. L. because he could not lobotomize or euthanize his alternative perspective and syntheses of what transpired around him. His coworkers seemed unperturbed at being immersed in the sticky trap of modern work. In his own case, R. L. had negotiated a sort of peace within, a demilitarized zone of not caring about the company, his cubical mates, his boss, or the ennui associated with the daily mindless tasks work required.

There was plenty of office drama and entertainment. From his midway station at cubicle 15, he enjoyed a central location to observe from 1 to 30, even numbers to the left-hand side of the corridor, odd to the right-hand side, with Joseph C. Dickerson, aka "Dickhead" at the head of it all, in a master cubicle extending fully from left to right, odd to even, at the top of a featureless corridor—the Lord of the Cubicons, as R. L. considered him.

It was sort of a portmanteau of "cubical" and "convict"—they were the inmates held prisoner at XYZ House of Detention and JCD was their warden from nine-to-five, Monday through Friday, for fifty-two weeks a year, 2080 work hours inclusive of vacation, sick time, and holidays. The word *cubicons* invoked *automaton*, which seemed to perfectly depict their numbered work existence, like parts in a catalogue of parts. Employee #1065-228 in cubical 15, just another part to be easily replaced should a gear-tooth fail or become unreliable and the machinery not perform. Sometimes, when his powers of auto-amusement were fully engaged, he referred to them all as *cubicoms*—comedic and comical residents of the cubicles, the troop of actors and actresses performing in the theater of the absurd. Other times, when he felt more sardonic, he thought of them collectively as *cubizoms*—cubical zombies mindlessly performing tasks, or *cubizombs*––working in a tomb, alive but trapped and oxygen-starved at their XYZ location. *Oh, death, spare me from this torture!* Not!

What, then, to do? Read below:

Rectum's Survival Tips, Part Two

- *If work is inane, don't dwell on it as this only leads to unhappiness. Instead, dwell on your unhappiness—that should cheer you up and take your mind off work.*

- *Call it like it is. If you drink the Kool-Aid and allow yourself to be deceived, you are drinking the poison of self-deception. Though you might appear to be alive, inside you slowly die. Check your pantry and put Kool-Aid on your shopping list if you are all out.*

- *Don't die...dye! Kool-Aid can be used as a colorful hair dye. Give it a try and surprise your coworkers and your boss. Start a blog, let us know how that worked out.*

- *Practice auto-amusement, a very useful tool for your survival toolbox. If you can't seem to find the auto-amuse feature in your living, breathing self, probe your navel and try harder. Wasn't that fun?*

At Home

Creature comforts and cohabitating creatures

His home, his sanctuary, his refuge from the part-time insanity of the world at large was by the yardstick of modern values quite modest. Surveying his kingdom of mostly used mismatched furniture and modern essentials such as a toaster, refrigerator and washer/dryer, he felt content. It was the same sort of contentment Aleksandr Solzhenitsyn referenced in his *One Day in*

the Life of Ivan Denisovich—another good day at
the gulag of modern society, and R. L.'s contentment was nearly effusive. After his Monday to Friday work routine, he rejuvenated at his own place,
well not quite––he rented––which was just fine
since pursuing the American Dream/Nightmare
of home ownership did not keep him up at night.
So what if his worn couch cushions smelled of ass.
At least it was his own ass. His meager possessions
were his. Try to achieve that under communism.
Capitalism in small doses worked well enough for
him and he had somehow managed not to get
sucked into the vortex of wanting more, a black
hole of near infinite pull that had the majority of
America in its gravitational attraction, relentlessly
pulling the unwary into a death-spiral void of un-
fulfilled desire—a Western model of existence that
had effectively been exported across the globe.

He even had a TV, more for decoration than actual viewing. Some time ago R. L. had concluded
that most available programming did not justify
an investment in his time, an actual precious commodity lost upon the producers of TV content.

There remained a sense of mystified bewilderment on his part when he overheard conversation about reality TV shows, game shows, soap operas, dramas, series and the assorted other programming options. The content simply had little or no nutritive value for his mind. The melt-in-your-mouth momentary sweetness, so ephemeral and never sustained, simply was insufficient to commit him to watching. The appeal others felt must have something to do with escapism—occupy one's mind with something mindless and they won't be thinking about much of anything. It is equivalent to this: Imagine stuffing your mouth with ersatz white bread—something masquerading as actual bread, the stuff some people try to live on—and then finding that there is no room in your mouth for anything resembling actual food.

TV news had little to do with serious journalism or providing unbiased information that constituted actual news. Still, there were exceptions—some programming with substance on *PBS*, the *History Channel*, *NatGeo*, and a few others. Given a more economical and selective cable package instead of bundled offerings of programming he eschewed and would never watch, much less pay for, he might be tempted to have a subscription. He did find *Al Jazeera* informative, but this only labeled him as a subversive in the eyes of others. Not that he cared, because he didn't. Sometimes ignorance was bliss. When he wanted to tune in and plug in and suffer through the commercials trying to sell him products and services he did not want or need in exchange for his money and the wink-wink deception of whatever lifestyle or experience the advertisement strove to convey, he could stream TV through the internet on his gaming console. Praise be to the scientists at *CERN,* with some help from Al Gore, for inventing the Worldwide Web. He realized webs were sticky, designed to trap prey in intricate interconnected strands of espionage and deceit. He preferred books and magazines.

In some strange twist of reality, which likely stemmed from the sense of humor of a supreme deity he was not sure existed, R. L. thought he himself would be an interesting subject for a true reality TV show. The nihilist at home; the nihilist at work; a non-conformist trying to conform in a world of perfumed non-substance; a part of, while still remaining apart from; simultaneously socially engaged and non-engaged in a non-conformist attempt to conform. He imagined the show sponsored by Huggies, so as to underscore, using the metaphor of an undergarment, just how challenging conforming to his delicate, yet somehow misshapen infant-body could be. Although it might prove difficult to contain the incessant stream of waste he prodigiously produced, Huggies would be fit for the task. Indeed, with the proper form-fitting adult incontinence brief anything was possible. Perhaps he could even play tennis without soiling himself. Even God, if he/she/it exists, would want to tune in, either for the show, the commercials, or both. R. L. himself would likely not be a regular viewer, much like a Nobel winning physicist would not attend a community college Physics 101 class to learn something. Not that this would be beneath him or undignified, but simply because he saw no benefit in watching in some voyeuristic, I-need-the-vicarious-experience sort of way. The commercials alone would not be sufficient for him to watch the show.

Today's list of chores included cleaning up, laundry, and literary exploration. In some ways, now that he owned his own washer-dryer duo, he missed the *Twilight Zone* experience of the previously coin-op, currently coinless, Suds-O-Matic, where he previously outsourced this task. The name seemed anachronistic, almost quaint, among the other business entities in that particular locale in the slum, where getting cleaned up generally meant going drug free. Amidst the dirt of the inner city, the Suds-O-Matic still stood, a bastion of cleanliness, or at least the garment of cleanliness draped over the grime of drugs, addiction, prostitution, gang violence, and the smelly sweat of survival in a tough neighborhood. He did rather miss the observational opportunities presented by the colorful cast of characters who regularly convened at the laundromat. But such was the sacrifice attached to moving past a washboard/ringer/clothesline, to a communal place to wash your underwear while negotiating a strange mix of socializing and non-socializing, all the way up to having his own means of laundering his own clothes in his own apartment. That's progress!

He read avidly and voraciously across a wide variety of genres. Today he delved into a new area of literature previously unexplored: paranormal romance. Despite the linguistic appeal of combining the words "paranormal" and "romance" in a nifty duet of marital delight, despite the flights of fanciful thoughts accompanying the notion of paranormal anything with the true and beautiful notions of Romanticism, and despite the horrific perversion of this unholy matrimony, he had never read a single bit of this particular literary style. Recognizing this glaring gap in his reading provoked a sort of itch that needed to be scratched, a curiosity, itself layered upon curiosity about his friend, Vanessa, who casually mentioned she had been enjoying a series of paranormal romances.

His friendship with Vanessa had no legitimate basis. They had no areas of common interest, no school connections, no vocational or avocational points of intersections. A sort of momentum, a Newtonian body in motion tends to stay in motion, non-directed continuity, characterized their friendship. Vanessa lived in a blissfully ignorant attitude about life and everything going on around her, a refreshing cluelessness that R. L. found mystifyingly alluring.

At first, he thought she was intellectually a bit vacuous; however, and notwithstanding that first impressions are lasting impressions, he eventually realized that was not it. There was more to Vanessa but it fell in the category of "less is more". She didn't know that she herself came across as astoundingly airheaded. Ever since Vanessa had moved to Secaucus, R. L. amused himself by referring to her as "Clueless in Secaucus" and wondered if Vanessa would even understand this cinematic reference. In R. L. 's worldview, Vanessa seemed to embody first-order incompetence. If true, this meant she was too dumb to even realize that she was dumb. For her to mention that she was reading piqued R. L. 's interest and challenged the airhead label he did not want to accept. He simply had to learn more about the genre she read, and perhaps gain some shred of insight into what lay beneath Vanessa's long auburn curls.

While the perfect hair, perfect teeth, and beautiful smile represented a very attractive package, something else attracted him beyond the Ivory Soap girl-next-door stereotype. It took some thoughtful pondering before it dawned on R. L. that Vanessa's sunny disposition and upbeat personality counterbalanced his own brooding moodiness. Insofar as opposites attract, he felt a strong attraction. It occurred to R. L. that the tether of nihilism had somehow bound them both, but from different ends. He looked at the world, sized things up, and largely recognized the meaninglessness and unimportance attached to what society valued. As a result, he mostly didn't care. On the other end of the spectrum, Vanessa didn't care because she did not take the time to reconcile herself to the world around her. She simply went about her day smiling and happy and unconcerned in a carefree manner. Beautiful!

"You think too much." Dimples punctuated either side of her flawless smile.

"You're right. I do." A frown adorned his sullen expression.

Night and day, yin and yang. He cataloged this fresh insight.

The book he had chosen at random had a somewhat discordant concoction of story elements represented on the back jacket. Actually, it was more of a mulligan stew, a hard to imagine Frankenstein of parts sewn together. A gluttonous vampire angel who apparently had been fighting vampire devils for a thousand years, which understandably left quite a bit of unsated appetite of desire, championed as the protagonist. For reasons not made entirely clear on the back jacket, this hero is now fighting the ISIS terrorist group. R. L. wondered if the Norse legions from Asgard or Valhalla might be part of the army to fight the modern Islamic extremists, but nothing was mentioned on the teaser synopsis. Instead, the protagonist travels to a dude ranch in Montana and becomes a cowboy. Good thing the chow wagon has some mighty fine vittles and other offerings, especially the cook. The vangel teleports with her to the tenth-century where insatiable attraction apparently accounts for the romance. Wow! Even better, the author was a *New York Times* best seller. He salivated as he cracked the spine...fascinating!

The paranormal romance turned out to be a real page-turner. Unfortunately, he had not read the previous books in the series. Periodically, he put the book down to transfer clothes from washer to dryer, aided by the helpful musical chime cheerily telling him the cycle was done. At other times, he paused his glued-to-the-page reading to get up to urinate, lamenting his lack of a form filling Huggies to preclude such interruption.

***

As he folded clothes on his dining room table, the only large horizontal expanse in his apartment, another drama unfolded in the periphery of his vision. Mephisto, his house gecko, stalked a meal

of crunchy cockroach. The wall-crawling predator liked to absorb some warmth from the dryer which must have then stimulated his appetite.
R. L. wasn't certain of Mephisto's gender, but it
hardly mattered. He or she functioned as the apex
predator, holding an infestation at bay. This lizard,
named after Faust's Mephistopheles, had replaced
Mr. Spock (or quite possibly Ms. Spock), jokingly
alluding to the lack of the creature's discernable
ears, who had unintentionally managed to pursue
his/her prey all the way into the confines of a roach
motel. Unfortunately, Mr./Ms. Spock never managed to check out. R. L. found the mummified
remains when he noted the lizard's absence after
a week or two. He got rid of all the Batesian motel accommodations for the native roaches before
getting Mephisto. It tipped the balance of power
slightly in favor of the insects, but the reptile still
held them at bay. He bore no resemblance to the
Geico gecko in color, and he stalked in relative
silence with no pseudo-British accent to warn the
roaches of impending doom.

The urban version of a *National Geographic* documentary unfolded and R. L. enjoyed the show. He even named the cockroaches, usually with some endearing first names like Georgette, Tommy, Bobbie, or Johnny. He watched as they scurried past his field of view––Mo, Larry, Curly, Betty, Suzie, or whatever name popped into mind. It was hard to tell them apart, but giving them names (it didn't matter if he assigned the correct gender) gave then a sort of identity. That humanity at times seemed to be a nameless host of bugs to the great predators of society, the rich corporate elites, the movers and shakers who would never name the faceless masses of humanity they often crushed underfoot without a second thought––R. L. would not allow such a microcosm to play out in his home.

In some Kafkaesque metamorphosis of shifting perspective, he understood the nightmarish reality of the modern world. The cockroaches had it right. They had been around much longer than the bipedals and would be around a long time after humanity's extinction, probably self-induced.

Under the influence of some fine dark German beer, he had even imagined himself as scurrying about, trying to avoid Mephisto, the equivalent of Godzilla, crushing and devouring his insect kin who remained powerless to stop the destruction. Still, by sheer numbers and reproductive capacity we, the cockroaches, would survive.

Lost in this reverie, R. L. methodically folded. He caught sight of Viktor, or possible Victoria, an unusually large and menacing roach that dared Mephisto to devour him. This Russian Mafioso of cockroaches had nothing to fear. The lizard climbed to a sunny spot on the wall on Velcro footpads and slept in well-fed contentment. Meandering thoughts turned to Velcro, a modern wonder inspired by the natural world and patterned after a burr, a marvel of adhesion and surface-to-surface cohesion. He loved the feel and sound of Velcro. There was something exquisitely visceral and satisfying about the sound of tearing it apart and marveling at how putting it back in place resulted in newfound strength and cohesion. The sound of ripping apart in endless repetition had a chop wood, carry water Buddhist quality of focus in the present moment. For a brief moment, he imagined himself in joyful contentment, in an Alzheimer demented state of late-life unawareness, repeatedly tearing apart the Velcro fastening of his adult incontinence Huggies-styled brief in unending joy and amazement.

The dryer chimed the end of another cycle and the final installment of clean linen beckoned to be unloaded. Life was good! And to make yours equally so, read on:

Rectum's Survival Tips, Part Three

- *There's no place like home. Even if it is in a ratty shit-hole cockroach-infested slum, you can still enjoy it.*

- *Little that is on television, whether it masquerades as news, comedy, or drama is actually entertaining or informative. If you feed your mind such drivel, you might be undernourished. Instead, read some para-*

normal romance.

- *If you have an indoor bug problem and are worried spraying pesticides might be additive to what you are already exposed to in the food you eat and somehow be unhealthy, a home lizard might be the answer; although, they might be illegal in your locale. Check first with the local pet authorities to be sure.*

- *If you like Hitchcock, Rod Serling, and Kafka, go to the local laundromat and enjoy yourself.*

Riding the Subway

Many feel that the subway is beneath them. It is.

Though he could not prove it, and he had no statistical references to disprove it, R. L. had a hunch that most of society viewed people who took the subway to work as somehow inferior, underprivileged, or unfortunate in the circumstances of their lives. After all, shouldn't you drive to work? Shouldn't you burn overpriced and overtaxed gasoline in a daily commute

to work, spending over half that time on idle or
in a mind-numbing traffic jam while giving or
receiving angry gestures towards rude and overly
aggressive, road-raged fellow motorists who seem
mystifyingly overly anxious to get to work considering most of them hated their jobs? This not even
accounting for tolls, car payments, maintenance
and repairs, depreciation, motor vehicle taxes, insurance, license and registration fees and, if you
commute in NYC, parking—just another hemor-
rhoidal reality of commuting. He had a difficult
time fathoming the whole car ownership schtick,
but recognizing that he had easy access to public
transportation, he didn't even need to own a car.
He did, however, have a driver's license, almost a
necessity for identification purposes in the Land of
the Free, and he had never had a ticket, at least not
a ticket for a good reason.

In college, he had borrowed a car and failed to
come to a full stop at an out-of-the-way intersec-
tion when no traffic in any direction, no pedestrians, and not even a stray dog shared the streets.
This didn't prevent a stealthily parked police offi-

cer from interrupting his bite of donut to ignite the flashing strobe and ridiculous siren of his unmarked police cruiser, scaring the bejesus out of R. L. and issuing him a traffic citation. Clearly, the end of the month neared and the officer's quota needed attention. R. L. just happened to be in the wrong place at the wrong time; however, the circumstances of this infraction did not escape notice of the automobile insurance company, who jacked up the rates on the unfortunate vehicle's owner.

R. L. realized that his affinity for the subway went beyond counterintuitive, countercultural sensibility. He didn't own a car, had a bad previous experience borrowing a car, eschewed the lack of courtesy displayed by the average NY driver, in addition to the aforementioned costs of owning and operating a car. But that wasn't why he rode the subway. Truth be told, he liked it. Yes, however dubious, convenient, or preposterous that might sound, he liked it. The subway station a couple of blocks away gave him an entry point to an entire network of subterranean transit. He felt the same way about riding the bus, except the subterranean part. At reasonable cost to him, some driver or engineer endured all the headaches and responsibility of operating the people mover, following a schedule, dealing with the crazies, and a whole lot of other aggravation. All R. L. had to do was grab a seat, or a pole, or a handhold, and enjoy the ride. Best of all, he got to watch people, a daily show of comedy and tragedy far more entertaining than anything Euripides or Sophocles might construct. The cost of admission amounted to nothing beyond the cost of public transportation, which incidentally he helped to subsidize thanks to government tax collection. In some sense, he amused himself by thinking he helped to pay for the actors and actresses who performed the human drama during his daily commute. Ticket to a Broadway play—why bother? Besides, he couldn't afford that kind of self-indulgent luxury, much less the concession prices.

Turning the table against the populace who staunchly believed that riding the subway was beneath them—it was actually underground—R. L. kind of felt a little sorry for people who chose not to avail themselves of the riches they failed to see. He shrugged. *C'est la vie.* He enjoyed the show in contradistinction to those unenlightened, disdainful masses who refused to take public transportation. Now, being an astute observer of human behavior, R. L. did not overlook the litter, the drunks, the purse snatchers, the panhandlers, the gangs, the hookers, and the boom-box carrying fellow passengers who obnoxiously insisted on blasting hip hop and loud bass with often uninspired lyrics. He saw them, and, of course, he heard them. It all represented drama on the stage, a panoply of sights and sounds. He especially liked graffiti––inspired urban art and screaming social messaging. Who needs YouTube when you have NYC public transportation?

It fascinated him... ride in vs. ride back, the similarities and the differences. R. L. had a sneaking suspicion that most of his fellow commuters did not share his enjoyment. Regardless. The ride was there for viewing pleasure as both spectator and participant, whether or not one chose to peer in on this slice of society. Yogi Berra, armchair

philosopher and Yankee great said, "You can observe a lot by just watching." R. L. practiced his
keen, well-honed observation skills on the daily
sojourn to and fro, from home to work, there and
back again. He saw the dull and defeated look on
some weary fellow subway mate. He considered
the glazed look on the woman across from him and
noted a similar glaze on the face of her service dog;
for a moment, he considered what life-circum-
stances she and her dog contended with. When
the two exited and a forlorn looking man reeking
of curry replaced her, R. L. had another person
to ponder. He speculated upon two strangers engaged in feigned-interest conversation, such disinterest evident in their nonverbal body language.
Or two passengers unsuccessfully pretending to
ignore one another.

Doors opened and closed, and each time his curiosity would ignite with fresh kindling. Not that
he cared about the life circumstances affecting and
afflicting his fellow passengers because he didn't.
Their lives were undoubtedly rife with meaninglessness, much like his own. However, observing

and pondering about the unique circumstances of a particular individual's meaningless life held some strange appeal. In this subway voyeurism, R. L. found a shred of meaning, a Monday through Friday anodyne antidote, an inoculation against the poison of the mundane and boring. The subway provided a refreshingly palatable and potable daily hydration. At times, it amounted to merely a sip, at other times, a deep draught. The subway commute never failed to be fresh and invigorating, a thirst quencher to start and finish his workday, bookends to negate the arid dehydration of his soulless work.

He watched with some annoyance and complete bemusement, the frenetic thumb texting of his fellow passengers, oblivious to the world around them, linked into and locked into a cellular world, void of true communication. He carried a flip phone, which he rarely used, not because he was some sort of Luddite; rather, this was a personal statement about his refusal to connect to the world through his phone, such engagement blinding him to what was actually going on right in front and to the side of him. He refused to be tuned-out by the apparent, but false, tuned-in world of cell phone "dialogue"—a non-engagement type of engagement, from his perspective.

The Twitter universe of sound bites, emojis, and 140-character tweets had completely disenfuckerated how we interact with fellow members of our species. A subway-riding segment of said species surrounded him daily. While his fellow passengers seemed disengaged, the opposite was true for R. L. The suits, the hairstyles and fingernails, the makeup and attire—all provided speculation for his curious mind. The man sleeping, the woman desperately trying to stay awake, the worried looks, the carefree attitude, the snippets of overheard conversation, constantly changing as doors opened and passengers exited while new commuters boarded, yielding an entirely new group upon which his mind could engage, watching the drama, appreciative of this particular moment in time.

To R. L., he shared camaraderie with the daily commuters, a part time brotherhood and sisterhood with the occasional commuters, and a special bond with selected few who recognized him and acknowledged him as a fellow traveler. While he preferred to claim a bit of turf sitting or grasping a pole or handle, he felt curious about the passengers who travelled between cars, on the move as though it would get them to their destination more quickly. He called them "walkers". They passed through to the next car, entering on one end and exiting on the other, a momentary guest appearance on the stage where he happened to be sitting or standing.

He considered himself a "watcher"––one who took a position from which to observe the surroundings in contradistinction to the majority of passengers who refused to make eye-contact in their self-absorbed existence. The "walkers" almost always had shifting eyes and gaze as they weaved their way through a crowded car, or briskly strode through an empty one. The stationary observer differed from the mobile observer only in style not in substance. One man in particular, he called "The Walker"—they had a special bond of sparsely spoken brotherhood. He and R. L. must have had a similar morning time to arrive at work. The Walker must have entered somewhere near the back of the train to begin his sojourn forward. R. L. liked to sit in a middle car, but he imagined the Walker getting on at a stop somewhere between his own entry with the shabbily attired slum dwellers, and the suits entering and embarking much closer to downtown.

Always, the conversation between the two was identical. The Walker entered from the back of the car, surveying the passengers as a predatory lion might look over a herd of gazelles. The two would make eye contact while simultaneously thrusting their chins slightly forward and upward.

"Hey." The Walker opened.

"Hey." The Watcher responded.

"Gotta keep movin'..."

R. L.'s subtle head nod of agreement completed the minimalist exchange.

Better than knowing the sun would rise in the East, the constancy and relative nothingness of this encounter presented endless nihilistic enjoyment for all that it represented in the simplicity of two human beings sharing a moment of connection. While R. L. fully appreciated that there was indeed a certain beauty in recognizing the collective commuter aura of, "I don't care about anything at this particular moment", a subway-car zeitgeist of public indifference, a sort of mass indifference on mass transit, *en masse*, this beauty paled when compared to what the Walker offered. In some non-bromance allusion to romanticism, the bond between Walker and Watcher typified ideal platonic love—two people bonded only by their shared, pure and unadulterated humanity. Not even R. L. could comprehend the depth of meaning in this seemingly meaningless encounter.

To make meaninglessness more meaningful, read on:

Rectum's Survival Tips, Part Four

- *Think less about where you are going and more about how you are going. Better yet, you are nowhere now and going nowhere. Doesn't that realization make you feel bet-*

ter?

- *You can be aggravated or amused—think AA—by the drama unfolding during life's daily travels. Pay attention and stop tuning-out in self-absorbed narcissism. Seriously?*

- *Life can pass you by when you are chronically sleep-deprived and in need of a nap. This could be a good thing if being passed by in life is something you aspire towards.*

- *If you miss your stop, keep going, or go back—either gets you somewhere. If that remotely makes any sense, re-read the first tip.*

- *For readers who do not have access to the subway, just pretend. Most people are very good pretenders. Then ride your pretend subway car, speaking to your pretend fellow passengers, all the way to your real psychiatry appointment.*

Respect for Your Superiors

You can diss someone artfully and openly with impunity and without consequence.

R. L. wondered about the many shades of gray between near-delusional inflated opinions of self-worth displayed by some, and near tragic low self-esteem displayed by others. He judged himself in an objective and critical way to be somewhere in between, well within the territory beneath the hallowed "normal distribution curve." It's complete hubris to think you are smarter than everyone around you, know more, or are more deserving. At least allow for the possibility that some people you deal with everyday might know a thing or two of their own.

Failure to acknowledge this possibility inevitably leads down a road littered with self-defeating feelings: no one appreciates me, sees my worth, understands how talented, smart, or wonderful I am, and so on down the road. Even the slightly more modest "a few people recognize my greatness, but not enough of them" is a path littered with corpses and death—those around you become dead to you in their failure to validate your worth and this invariably leads to a strange sort of death to oneself. If you don't feel good about yourself, why would you think, or much worse—EXPECT—other people to think you're smart or wonderful or fill in the blank for whatever self-image you want to feel good about yourself. Feel good and don't give a flying f#%k what other people think. Same thing in reverse--stop passing judgment, usually in some self-aggrandizing manner, about everyone else. If you enjoy being judge, jury, and executioner, you've probably already been condemned to a death sentence by a similarly inclined colleague.

So what if they are smarter. So what if they only think they are smarter. So what if they are prettier, drive a better car, are better dressed, or fill in the blank however you want to. So what if they think they are. So what if you think that way about yourself, a thought born in some world of comparison among non-equals to ego-inflate the self-image of whoever happens to be thinking that way. Do you think the universe cares?

Accept the fact, or at least the opinion, that some people you deal with every day of your life are somehow superior to you, which in a potentially devastating ego-deflating way makes you inferior to them. So what? Who cares? If you do, spend more time in the imaginary head-space of Rectum Leviticus. He respects his superiors. He even respects his inferiors. Truth is, he doesn't buy into these labels of human skill, pseudo achievement, and potential. He has learned to do his own thing and he likes doing it, especially at work, and especially when it comes to his boss.

Now, Joseph C. Dickerson was not a bad man. To make such a statement would expose an underlying value system which inevitably puts one set of values or beliefs or delusions against another—corpses and all manner of dead things are rotting and strewn all along that path. Was he a good boss? In R. L.'s estimation, that was all a matter of perspective. The Lord of the Cubicons undoubtedly thought he was a terrific boss. He'd been to management training seminars and self-help courses in human relations; he even dabbled a bit in some leadership courses. The higher ups at XYZ had invested in Dickhead's corporate career, not realizing that he had already Peter Principled his way as far up the ladder of corporate achievement as even a dysfunctional company could tolerate.

Given the sterile oppression of the company's rules and regulations governing all manner of workforce behavior, expression, clothing, hair style, jewelry, sexual harassment, cultural tol-

erance, non-discrimination, and workplace violence––to name a few—Dickhead thought he was
an excellent boss and role model. He followed the
rules, knew them stone-cold, as though he needed to quote from Starfleet's tome of regulations.
The company document must be a terabyte long,
enough to fill even Dickhead's oversized double
cubicle with carefully thought out rules governing
the operations and conduct of pretty much everything. Euphemistically, employees referred to ses-
sions with the boss as a little R & R. Such encounters were disciplinary in nature; thus, the R & R of
rules and regulations epitomized the antithesis of
rest and relaxation.

Once, R. L. had the misfortune of passing flatus
just as his boss meandered down the corridor. A
somewhat hushed and surreptitious spontaneous
meeting ensued as Mr. Dickerson pointed to the
master cubical. Time for some R & R. A recita-
tion of workplace conduct behavior policy designation HR: 102, subsection F, part iii followed.
Mr. Dickerson quoted HR: 102, F, iii, *ff* verba-
tim, pausing only long enough to breathe between

paragraphs. The policy addressed workplace fart-
ing in diplomatic language. Somehow, this did not
lead to another entry into his disciplinary file, but
it did constitute a "verbal warning."

In part, R. L. understood why he had garnered
that previous reprimand for a dress code violation.
His standard issue XYZ shirt with its uniform pea-
cock-blue color and uninspired generic logo had
a coffee stain. It mattered not to Dickerson that
an inattentive subway passenger had spilled her
spiced pumpkin latte while attempting to text her
boyfriend, with R. L. standing well within her
personal perimeter zone of bubble-like self-pro-
tection, a fellow commuter who did not want to
invade the young woman's personal space, but the
commute happened to be unusually crowded that
morning. She didn't even apologize; instead, looking at him as though he deserved it for breaching
her invisible perimeter, she completed her text, put
the phone in her purse, and huffed. Of course,
Mr. Dickerson wanted to hear none of it. The
proximate cause stood as irrelevant in his mind
and way of thinking. Rectum had violated blah,

blah, blabeddy, blah of policy blah, blah, blabbeddy, blah governing proper attire. So be it.

While he understood enforcement, chain of command, and having a superior, and while he wasn't walking in Dickhead's shoes, the selective application of policies, procedures, rules and regulations did irk him at times. Everyone at work knew that Mike in cubical 7 sometimes looked at porn during his breaks. Even Mr. Dickerson knew it. The rumor was Mike had unintentionally walked into Mr. D's double-cubical, rather boldly hit the "enter" button restoring a darkened screen on the boss' computer monitor, and guess what? Mike didn't have any reprimands in his work file. Terry, cubical 24, liked to internet shop, Chrissy (not 22, the one in 18) occasionally surfed the net. R. L. couldn't quote the policies, but clearly these were workplace violations, but somehow, in some management workshop, the Lord of the Cubicons must have learned it's important to show some humanity.

Mike also liked to suck up to the boss in some sycophantic manner as they discussed football.

Both of them lived, breathed, ate, and shat football. Thursday night football, weekend football,
Monday night football, and a steady diet of fan-
tasy football. Marx had it right: the opium of the
people, but it wasn't religion anymore—football
provided all the narcotic of religion with an added
gratifying splash of action. In grammar school, R.
L. had a classmate who knew the statistics on hun-
dreds of league players, the team schedules, and
an encyclopedia of other football facts and figures.
In later life, R. L. realized that that classmate was
probably an idiot savant; maybe he had scored a
job as an analyst for ESPN. Who the f#%k knows
and, more importantly, who the f#%k cares? In
answer to this rhetorical question: guys like Joseph
and Mike, and millions of other football enthusiasts.

   They competed in a certain one-upsmanship
to knowing and demonstrating football knowledge—a clear attempt to prove one's superiority
on the field, besting your opponent in their flailing
ignorance by spouting some obscure statistical fact
or referencing the name of the kicker who booted

the potentially winning field goal during game six of the regular season twelve years ago. R. L. didn't care, but he overheard the heated watercooler conversation his boss, in an effort to share his humanity and his superiority, sometimes engaged in. The tome of Starfleet Academy was dwarfed by the combined tome of NFL and NCAA football stats. (Can't escape the damn alphabet soup!) Even James T. Kirk would be proud to have the mastery and command of Joseph C. Dickerson when it came to quoting football facts. It only reminded R. L. of how the once svelte and commanding captain of the USS Enterprise had fallen so far in the public zeitgeist by now hawking discounts on commercials. My, what a fall from grace for the overweight captain––not to the blimp-out level of some former celebrities, but still quite rotund.

What the hell. R. L. had a whole series of strategies when Dickhead acted like one, such as when his boss earnestly invoked Patrick Stewart with an imitation of, "Make it so..." trying to cajole and entreat R. L. into performing an impossible feat. In the past, when he had less tolerance and less well

ingrained nihilistic tendencies, R. L. would silently think, *Eat shit and die,* while simultaneously
saying aloud, "Yes, sir."

Last year he had listened to a National Geographic show and had learned a new word—co-
prophage. He liked words and this had become
one of his favorites because of all the possibilities it
presented. Coprophagia means to consume feces.
Dung beetles are coprophages. So are rabbits, but
what is particularly curious about rabbits is they
have two different kinds of feces. The one they
produce during the day is apparently not for proper cuisine; however, their night feces is consumed;
although, only a rabbit could say if it is consumed
with delight. Here is a nice tasty carrot and next to
it some pellet of night excrement—which do you
prefer?

"Eat shit and die" seemed too disrespectful a
retort, even to silently hold your tongue in check
and just think it. He recalled reading an expression in a book somewhere, an exclamation in response to some insult, "Pick corn out of your
own shit and eat it." Demonstrably, that is a more

sophisticated retort. Now, when Mr. Dickerson was being unreasonable, R. L. responded, "Copraphagic!" entirely confident his boss remained clueless regarding the corn-picking, rabbit-eating metaphor he conjured. At other times, he resorted to a different and even more exquisite diss, one that appealed to R. L.'s devious and self-amusing mind—"Smegaliscious!" Again, he remained confident and self-assured that such reference to the sebaceous crud that accumulates beneath a man's uncircumcised foreskin went beyond his boss's understanding. Living in a world of obscure words and knowing how to enjoy them accounted for one of R. L.'s simple pleasures.

Of course, Dickhead undoubtedly thought quite highly of himself when he verbally chastised R. L. by smugly suggesting, "Rectum, you are so close to being a complete..." He never finished the sentence, but proudly knew the final word was "asshole" and he knew R. L. got the reference. Of course, Dickhead would be in violation of workplace policy blahdibly blah on harassment, and policy blahdibly blah on profanity if he was actually ballsy enough to complete the sentence. However, Mr. Dickerson's skill at verbal repartee maxed out by such a unilateral exchange. Receiving his boss's innuendo, an Italian suppository of sorts, administered by the wordplay of Rectum's first name, constituted an insult, but it represented an opportunity as well. At such times, R. L. wanted to punch his boss. Not physically make a fist and strike him; that was by far too crude. "Punch" here referred to another of R. L.'s favorite expressions, a metaphorical visualization, "Like a turd floating in a punchbowl." Following such an insult, R. L. simply conjured the punchbowl in his mind's eyes and would respond, "I'll try not to be, sir." It sounded conciliatory. Hardly! He vividly watched his boss floating alongside, a punch with no physical contact but hitting the mark none the less.

If his boss acted in some over-the-top, particularly egregious way, R. L. would simply roll up his sleeve to the tattoo on his forearm and point. To the unwary, it appeared that the tattoo was three letters spelling, F-U-N. The beauty and brilliance of Berlin Sans FB font is the "Y" looks a lot like a

"U"—F-Y-N, his subtle pointed response miscon-
strued as an entreaty for his boss to try and have
more fun, when in fact, it was R. L.'s cryptic message telling his boss, "FUCK YOU NOW!" Rectum felt certain such response violated no workplace rule, regulation, policy, or procedure unless he had somehow overlooked one admonishing
and outlawing making fun of your boss by referring to things he is clueless about. It's important to
respect your superiors, especially your boss, even if
he is a bit of a pretentious twat waffle. And to do
so while smiling within, read on:

Rectum's Survival Tips, Part Five

- *Respect your superiors even if they don't
  really deserve your respect; it's all a matter
  of perspective. Not! Cultivate an air of superiority and expect others to grovel before
  you and toss rose petals where you tread.*

- *Amuse yourself with visualizations and
  application of obscure words, not to embark*

on a journey of self-superiority, but rather to embark upon a path of self-entertainment. Only do this if you have no money for more socially acceptable means of entertainment.

- Enjoy football if that's your thing, but understand not everyone shares your zealous enthusiasm. Start a club, wear an armband, crowdsource the "I am football challenged" movement.

- Just because occasionally you might have to eat shit, this does not mean you have to develop a taste for it. If you do develop such a taste, perhaps the rabbit is your spirit totem. If you do happen to eat some shit (let's not forget that hotdogs reportedly contain a measurable but rather small amount of rat feces) minty mouth wash should theoretically neutralize your circumstance. Stock up, especially at work.

The Supermarket

So much choice—a watering hole of essential entertainment

The supermarket captures so much about what modern society values and how it operates. R. L. enjoyed his trips there all-the-while sustaining a type of love-hate relationship. Gone were the days of locally produced and harvested foods and the entire small market environment where villagers could interact in humanly meaningful ways. Long gone were the times of forag-

ing and hunter-gathering, when food and suste-
nance required certain true survival skills. These
had been replaced by superstores of multiple similar offerings distinguished primarily by differences
in fancy and expensive packaging and product
placement within the environs of the market.

Supermarkets are vast indoor deserts, with un-
countable food items like grains of sand, yet still
beckoning in a wasteland devoid of the quenching
waters of meaningful human interaction. Harried
shoppers rushed through aisles while managing
children, shopping carts, cell phones, and negotiating other similarly burdened fellow shoppers.
Hunting nowadays referred to finding a parking
space or a so-called bargain, folks apparently ignorant that whatever discount is reflected in a
so-called bargain, is more than made up for by other overpriced merchandise. They, the nameless and
faceless marketing and promotion experts, did not
fool R. L. He had developed an immunity to the
tricks and techniques of trying to sell something
he neither wanted nor needed, preying upon unwary manipulation of shoppers' desires for status,

a brand name, clever advertising, and so on. He fancied himself as a stealth undercover usurper of all those marketing efforts while he remained in plain sight.

Typically, he was highly selective in his purchases, scanning the weekly circular for loss leaders, only using coupons on items he needed while passing on the multitude of promotions for things he did not. Since he walked to and from the market, he mentally weighed, measured, and arranged items within his backpack as he strolled through the supermarket aisles. Often, he purchased generic and lower shelf items figuring the less savvy shoppers were subsidizing the product placement on corner displays and at eye-level. Finding tasty produce, especially ripe fruit, instead of the tasteless-but-ships-well genetically bred and selected for ease of transport varieties that predominated always presented a bit of a challenge.

He eschewed pre-prepared microwaveable, loaded with extra salt and preservatives fast food dinners. He actually enjoyed preparing food for himself, spiced and flavored according to his own preferences instead of market research. He bought in bulk using reusable bags and containers. While he withheld judgment on the naïve shoppers, he liked to amuse himself by counting the types of nearly identical items. Twenty-six varieties of bar soap, eighteen types of dog food split evenly among the dry and the wet, but only fifteen types of cat food—something was going on there and he speculated it had to do with the extra shelf space devoted to cat and kitty litter of which there were eleven varieties in his local store. No gecko food, collars, cages, toys or other sundry items, but fortunately Mephisto remained ignorant of this slight. He (or possibly she) still remained true to the hunter-gatherer roots that made supermarket shopping pre-obsolete, an interesting and some-what nostalgic concept.

Why people would shop for lawn furniture, or a gas grill, or an extension cord at a supermarket puzzled him slightly. Isn't that what a hardware store is for? It made R. L. wonder if Home Depot would soon be selling chicken fillets and out of season strawberries.

He liked to read food labels and catalogue the obscure ingredients. What is the effect of drinking sodium silicialuminate? Was he drinking too much, too little, or just enough—a Goldilocks and the Three Bears conundrum? This reminded him to buy some more porridge. Still, he found himself wondering if cumulative consumption of food preservatives would ultimately make embalming a dying profession, more so than it already was.

Entertainment abounded at the checkout lane, always fraught with drama. A shopper ahead on the 15-items-or-less express lane obviously violated that limit, much to the consternation of the next-in-lane who had only three purchases. As one shopper fumed, ready to chastise the rule breaker, but concerned that the rule breaker could be armed or might be a tire slasher, restraint prevailed and the rule-following shopper stewed in unrequited hate. Her eyes spewed venom as she impatiently waited, a victim of a checkout line miscreant. R. L. watched in bemused fascination as the woman with excess items counted off fifteen and placed a space bar on the conveyor belt to separate the remaining ten or so items. Three-item Jane Doe fumed at this exploitation of a loophole, while the ahead woman checked out twice. The cashier remained oblivious.

Once, R. L. had asked if two one-quart containers of 2% milk counted as one item or two. He wondered about things like this but the cashier answered with a shrug. Who cares? R. L. was a bit younger and less nihilistic then. Now, he didn't care and he realized how utterly meaningless the question actually was. He didn't care how items were counted or whether or not the person ahead of him had a few extra items. There were more important things to care about, like the tabloid headlines. No rush to conclude his shopping extravaganza, important newsies drew his attention.

Divorce and broken relationships, royalty gossip, affairs, secret babies, paparazzi-captured weight gain, and extraterrestrials ruled the celebrity stories adorning the final shopping zone before checkout. How totally juicy! These are obviously what most people want to be up on or else why would the corporate marketeers place these fifth-grade reading level publications at such a pivotal place within the store? Adjacent to print gossip, the other high priority essentials beckoned: candy, chewing gum, Chap Stick, and breath mints, of which there were only a disappointing twelve different types to select from. On this particular shopping excursion, R. L. spotted a package of condoms sandwiched among the mints. "Condom mints," he thought to himself; shouldn't these be with the ketchup, mustard, and other condiments? Was this a store patron's idea of a joke? If so, he would like to meet that person. More likely, among the essential items in the shopper's cart, the condoms simply did not make the final cut when economic constraints prevailed. R. L. wondered what decision-making algorithm was utilized prior to the end result of leaving the condoms behind. He conjectured how the mystery shopper might have deliberated. What do I leave behind: the six-pack of lite beer, the bar soap, toilet paper, can of tasty salmon cat food, latest issue of *National Enquirer,* or the Trojan super-sensitive, lubed, ribbed condoms? What calculus could possibly determine what to keep and what to leave behind? Enquiring minds want to know.

The reverie only broke as his turn came to check out. He looked at his receipt amazed at how much money he had saved--$36.20 on this $41.62 purchase. "How do they manage to stay in business?" he quipped silently.

His final stop prior to exiting always brought stares of disbelief from fellow shoppers. Those entering and sanitizing their shopping cart handles with antibacterial wipes, made available in homage to collective mysophobia, and those exiting in a hasty and harried rush to their next task, all paused to watch R. L. as he ripped off the unnecessary cardboard boxes and other assorted packaging and threw them away. Bare and naked essentials fit better in his backpack and in his limited cabinet space at home. Another trip to the market had ended. And if the supermarket aisles do not have the survival items you need, be sure to read on:

Rectum's Survival Tips, Part Six

- *If you are a savvy supermarket shopper, share you shopping tips on our crowd-sourced public domain website: www.IamasavvysupermarketshoppinggeekandIcanhelpyou.info and qualify for a two-for-one discount coupon.*

- *Enjoy your supermarket experience. Would you prefer lurking by the watering hole, spear in hand, waiting for an unsuspecting antelope to wander along?*

- *Read food labels if you want to build your vocabulary, impress your friends, and excel at Scrabble.*

- *Who was the last person to touch the sanitizing wipe dispenser and where have their hands been? Enquiring minds want to know and so should you.*

Under the Influence

The uninhibited mind revealed in the fog of cognitive impairment.

Sometimes, within the confines of his home sanctuary, he overindulged. Spaten Optimator remained as his preferred method to ease into the temporary calm, a balm to numb the insanity pervading modern culture. When this occurred, the lapse in self-discipline seemed somehow to creep up unaware, much like a commando in camouflage stealthily moving towards a particular target. Before he realized that he had succumbed to foggy thoughts and disparate connections, he found himself unaware and under the influence.

Mephisto cocked his/her head to the side, cautiously assessing the extent of inebriation.

"What are you looking at?" The mumbled and jumbled words, full of suspicion, remained unanswered as Mephisto's attention became distracted by a scurrying roach.

On such occasions, R. L. led a Frito Lay existence of chips and bliss. Deliverance came not through lite beer, the equivalent of what he imagined to be a dog drinking its own piss, straw amber in a bottle or perhaps a moronic aluminum dildonic cylinder providing fancy packaging to deceive the imbiber into thinking the contents masquerading within was perhaps something resembling a brew worthy of consumption. No! He drank a full-bodied dark German formula with Black Forest mud, grain, and hops in some medieval witch's concoction of intoxicating insanity. The chips inexplicably incited a raging thirst for swirling bubbling dark madness best imbued from a stein, leaving froth and semi-quenched desire dressing his lips.

Only then could he attempt to read the news of the day, fully aware of the brainless, mindless zombie content, the vaporous annulment of any intelligence fed to the masses as pablum to mum and stymie with ersatz pseudo food feeding a ravenous pseudo reality. Surely a neurotoxin lay within the electron stream lighting the digital display before him, a perfidious and nefarious stream of ones and zeros surpassing even country music and grits in the ability to suppress creativity, an ultimate synaptic block.

Kardashian this, Kardashian that, with an overdose of pop star *de jeur*, flavor of the month, icon of the moment to eviscerate any thought processes, and don't forget to OD some more on a Princess whose name he could not recall, or her hair style, or particular dress she wore to some non-event, because his mind had numbed itself in a desperate attempt at self-preservation. Tell me more about some never-heard-of-before celebrity and the reason for his/her child's incarcera-

tion—his mind clamored in mounting inebriation. Years prior, incessant OJ news coverage juiced
R. L.'s neurons one time too many and no amount
of libation in his stein could undo the damage, but
it could anesthetize the effect slightly. Diana, his
last Duchess, and the relentless coverage of everything Royal Family had caused irreparable brain
scarring that had mercifully established itself, im-
munizing him against further decay.

The addictive quality of the digital neurotoxin
affecting the masses left him with no misconcep-
tions about the state of our world. The zombie
apocalypse had already occurred, vectored by a
brain-eating virus infecting smart phones. There's
a bit of irony—a smart phone, probably a tru-
ism considering how brain dead users had become,
succumbing to an onslaught of streaming digital downloads sucking out their brains and now
rampaging as a mindless hoard, hungry for more
brain.

He sipped and savored while munching on
another chip, momentarily surfing a wave of
bliss only to suffocate in the undertow of Girls

Gone Wild, coeds frolicking on a hardly pristine Ft. Lauderdale beach at spring break, falling prey to testosterone-crazed, cocaine-snorting, Lite beer-drinking Gen XYZers who wink vapid emojis of sincerity. Hardly. His guilt-free spring break escapades were imaginary memories he never had, providing only fodder for what remaining neurons had managed to escape the digital onslaught of vectored self-absorbed lobotomizing news, not to mention the Pinterest-Instagram-Facebook drivel that assaulted all his sensibilities and gave just argument to sterilization and gun violence to purge humanity of this collective affliction.

How to inoculate and unindoctrinate against this mindless madness and thereby free himself of the burden of endless hanging chad? How to mollify his sense of outrage at the vacant sensibilities of modern culture and society, and replace that with the real-world version of reality TV, absent commercials attempting to pollute and manipulate vacated thought into purchasing an unneeded commodity to prop up a failing economic Ponzi scheme of indebtedness? He took a deep draught while severing his internet connection to the World Wide Web of deception. He resisted the under-the-influence urge to subscribe to a web portal of like-minded revolutionaries.

The nihilist within clamored to shrug it all off and not care but it troubled him. Like a tongue incessantly probing a cracked tooth, feeling the unfamiliar jagged edges attempting to fathom some familiarity, his thoughts returned willingly and unwillingly to the absurdity of his current dilemma, a mockery of mentation, a Rubik's cube of puzzlement, the ongoing splinter in his mind. Who, what, when, where, if, how, why—the seven questions keying the philosopher's stone guarding the tomb of his imagination, sentries blocking the tidal force waiting to be unleashed upon...upon...upon who, what, when, where, if, how, why—an aberrant nihilistic tautology, the paradox of his existence. The deep and abiding caring of not caring remained as a psychic and soul burden he shouldered with only partial indifference.

Crunch, munch, sip, stew, brew, and brood. There had to be answers to solve this riddle of the Sphinx, an imponderable endless Mobius strip twisting and turning upon itself *ad infinitum* and beyond. Could he reverse engineer the answers by working back to the questions, or must he roll the stone uphill *ad nauseam* like a Sisyphean automaton destined to ongoing failure and frustration? Could he instead allow the stone to roll downhill, gathering speed with the g-force of relentless momentum carrying it ever downward, with mounting speed and anxiety to crash and crush with deadly force upon the guardians, or the opposite, the antithesis? Should he allow the tombstone to accelerate beyond escape velocity, propelled by some unseen force of will and psyche, to float amidst the detritus orbiting the blue planet of our home, inexorably succumbing to the pollution of society, a scourge threatening to purge humanity of its own toxic existence? The kinetics of destruction seemed somehow to mirror the kinetics of escape, a red pill/blue pill choice in the conundrum of this matrix. Ah, Horatio, to be or not to be? Shall we flip a coin?

Quite possibly, he teetered on the edge of madness. He preferred to think he was going sane. There was a sane solace in the void of not knowing, not thinking, not imagining, not closing any synapses with a neurochemical transmitter of insight. He created the wardens guarding the prison of mentation, but he refused to hand the keys over to the mass media of propaganda, leaving himself in control, or at least some illusory notion of such, a phantom, a shadow without true form or substance yet quite possibly the means of escape, a non-answer to a non-question in some mirror universe of absurdity.

He pondered the imponderable. If you feed yourself junk will you regurgitate junk? What about chips? If you feed yourself chips what happens? Can you nibble on the kibbles and bits of modern society without vomiting? Can you digest the great and noble truths without getting indigestion? At such moments, free floating anxiety melded into free floating consciousness of absurd ideas and postulates and discordant inebriation.

Stop seeking answers. Stop asking questions. Stop time which has no existence other than as a concept, an H. G. Wellian notion of a linear universe, a fourth dimensional construct without material or energetic substance, naught, zero, less than nothing as nothing is conceptually something. Another paradox, but he felt himself peeling back the veil, exposing for just a moment, no, a non-moment of recognition, an infinitesimal uni-dimensional dot of awareness, a speck of non-substantial substance free of time and mass, non-temporal, non-physical, non-corporeal, the nothingness of all that is, was, and could be.

Crunch, sip, munch, sip, chop wood, carry water. He caught a rainbow and realized the string attaching his world was merely a thread that he scissored with perfect aplomb and witnessed the prison bars dissolve along with the imaginary sentries. A dual recognition and non-duel awareness engulfed him in a veritable tsunami of comfort and sanity. Under the potent influence of the German elixir, he finally figured out there was nothing to figure out. Nada-nirvana... Nihilistic bliss!

He gulped brown liquid inspiration from the stein, placed it down with a thud, and belched unceremoniously, content that he would sleep well tonight.

Mephisto studied him in R. L. 's imagined fascination, passing no judgement on the morality of this intoxication, but withdrawing to the safety of the ceiling while surveying the scene below. A cockroach army of fast-moving Bradley tanks amassed behind hidden enemy lines where general Viktor masterminded an attack upon the enemy lizard. A mindless hoard of insect zombies gathered––not the slow, bumbling creatures of Hollywood old; rather, the nimble Hussain Bolt versions, directed *en masse* by the Russian kingpin. For a brief moment, R. L. felt the reptilian fear of this potential assault, alone, without reinforcement or succor while his nemesis plotted and planned. The gecko blinked, or was it a wink?

Gazing upward, he intoned, "Don't worry, Mephisto, I'll protect you." A tear welled. "I'll proprect you, my little buddy. We gotta...hic-cup...glook after each rother."

Thoughts floundered in alcoholic mist. In-sights flashed then faded. He sipped, savored, then promptly fell asleep, with head resting upon the coffee table and Frito residue coloring his chin. And from this haze of mental fog and golden crumbs, these insights can be gleaned:

Rectum's Survival Tips, Part Seven

- *Dark German beer is both delightful and dangerous.*

- *What is the relationship between the verb "brood" and the noun "brood"? Grab a six-pack and ruminate on this but don't count chickens before they hatch. If this last sentence makes no sense, you are not far enough into your six-pack. If it does make sense, you are too far along in your six-pack.*

- *Time flies like an arrow. Fruit flies like a*

banana.

- *The balm of intoxication is but a temporary salve to ease the pain of awareness. Yet, the intoxication of blissful unawareness has a definite appeal. (see character Vanessa in chapter 3)*

THE NEXT DAY

When the anesthetic wears off, pain follows.

He recalled a snippet from a Monty Python sketch he had come across years ago, though he could not recall any details beyond a single statement, "My brain hurts."

"Ouch!" That was the problem with that dark German beer. While it mollified and both lusciously and deliciously calmed and confused his thoughts into delightful bouncing rubber-band balls of loftiness and descent, the following day was hell to pay. A hangover.

Last night he danced with some buxom flirtatious *Fräulein*, enjoying every word of her frivolous thoughtless meanderings. Today, her silly laughter morphed into ridiculously loud commands barked from the merciless voice box of a female uniformed SS Nazi officer who didn't give two shits, or even one small brown rabbit turd, that his head pounded worse than a Japanese Taiko drum.

Silently, he cursed the stein, not because it had left an indelible water ring at its base, marking and marring forever his cheap wooden coffee table from Ikea. Momentarily he winced at redoubled pain as he recalled the intricate, tedious, tortuous assembly the table had demanded. "Some assembly required", a devil-spawned mockery of his pathetic non-skills with power tools and even simple hand implements such as a screwdriver. Eight hours of murderous torture later he had completed the dirty deed, but not before he contemplated jumping out the window having penned a cursory suicide note with a Clue to his final demise, "IKEA, in the living room (he unfortunately did not have a conservatory), with the hammer." Yet, his survival instinct had prevailed, and he had somehow managed to complete the project *sans* tossing himself or a partially assembled coffee table out the window.

At some primal level, he had convinced himself that he most likely, or at least fairly probably, could be passible with some primitive rock-derived tools that his Neanderthal ancestors were undoubtedly proficient with. A thought followed, leaving him disturbed, brain pounding, without solace, and staring at his ring-water-mark adorning the wood veneer. Neanderthals had real tools like knives and spears and snares and their men were strong and muscular, at least at the Museum of Natural History diorama, which only highlighted how wimpy and incompetent this Cro-Magnon scion had evolved or devolved to. Perhaps *Homo Australopithecus* provided a better prototype for his manly aspirations.

He hunched forward bending in a semi-erect position, allowing his knuckles to touch the pile on the worn olefin carpet. The light and angle somehow aligned. *Impossible! There is simply no f'in way,* he thought to himself. Yet there, unmistakably patterned into the stained tabletop, the image was plain to view. Even an atheist could see the resemblance—Jesus in half-profile, haloed and smiling. R. L.'s bleary eyes began to tear at the miracle of the coffee table for which he was the first and only privileged witness. Could this be the next Fatima? Or something like that crying statue in Peru or somewhere? At this moment of newfound religious fervor, he blanked on where that particular statue and the lines of the devout worshipers were actually located. Surely, this was more profound and relevant than the face of Jesus in that pizza baked in the Bronx, or was it New Jersey—hell, what does it matter anyway?

As this silent thought left his mind, the universe responded, the light shifted. He blinked. The image had dissolved as mysteriously as it had appeared. When he cocked his head to the side, trying to find the precise angle to recreate the icon, the best he could manage was a facsimile of Elvis grinning and a rather poor one at that. Obviously, he was not worthy, or this represented yet another cosmic joke. All the strength he could muster brought him fully upright, wondering why it was so bright even with the shades drawn and why the clock ticked so loudly. Balancing after a brief wobble—Weebles wobble but they won't fall down—he managed to make it to the bathroom.

A worrisome crunch stopped him. He feared the worst. Surely, Mephisto's frail skeleton would not crunch thus. Could this be Kim, or Donny, or some other unnamed insect with a frangible exoskeleton? Even Viktor deserved better than such a crushing defeat. With trepidation, he lifted his foot and relief washed over him. An errant chip lay pulverized to become eventual food for the insect hoard. He gasped in audible relief.

The image looking back from the bathroom mirror only vaguely resembled his best recollection of the last time he reflected upon himself. Stubble, dried spittle and possibly some vomit caked his chin with adherent golden chiplets. His misbuttoned shirt and slept-in clothes, wrinkled and disheveled, stared back, the visage of a once proud *Homo Sapiens.* Pathetic! Positioned on the wall over the mirror, Mephisto seemed to smile in reptilian disapprobation. Head cocked, tongue flicked, and a fly met its demise. Nature can be cruel and unforgiving; it occurred to R. L. that the same could be said about life. Is saber-toothed tiger vs. Neanderthal that different than lizard-on-the-wall vs. fly-on-the-wall? As Mephisto swallowed and licked his lizard lips, R. L. answered his own question with a resounding, "Yes!" Brains over brawn were essential to survival. Looking in the mirror he felt reassured, as brawn did not gaze back, but he did detect some manly-looking facial hair.

"Damn those German brewmasters!" He said it aloud, surprised at first that his left-brain speech center somehow still communicated with his mouth and larynx. Suddenly, he became acutely conscious of how arid his tongue seemed, along with a positively wretched sensation assaulting his taste buds. *Strange, I don't recall smoking a cigar and licking the ashtray.* A fear gripped him with the momentary conjecture that he might have licked the cheap olefin pile trying to consume crumbs from an overturned and empty bag of Doritos he remembered seeing on the floor beneath the now ephemeral smiling Jesus transfigured into a mocking grotesque icon of blue suede shoes. Reaching for desperately needed oral care, salvation lay in a bottle of Scope hiding within his medicine cabinet. As he opened wide before swishing liquid blue minty deliverance, he caught site of orange smearing his upper incisor, no doubt the remains of red dye #8, a staple of snack foods.

Tending to his oral needs, he suddenly felt gratified. Headache subsiding, he stood fully erect as a proud *Homo Erectus* now sapient and grinned mightily. His mirror visage smiled back. "Damn those Germans are awesome! Whoever brewed that shit should get a Nobel prize!"

He grabbed his worn copy of *Uncle John's Bathroom Reader,* enthroned himself, and got down to business. This tome contained certain wisdom of the ages. He leisurely reread dog-eared sections concentrating on the mechanics and uses of simple tools and the impact on human evolution.

If you, too, want to navigate in the wake of indiscretion, read on:

Rectum's Survival Tips, Part Eight

- *Dark German beer is both delightful and dangerous. Be prepared for the aftermath of overindulgence.*

- *A minty mouthwash covers a multitude of sins.*

- *Purchasing items requiring self-assembly may lead to suicidal thoughts.*

- *There are no credible reports of Jesus or Elvis appearing on coffee tables, or other household items such as towels or pizza boxes. Learn to see the miraculous in the mundane and ordinary.*

- *Uncle John's Bathroom Reader is essential equipment to accessorize the rest room sanctuary.*

DRAMA AT WORK

Astronomy dethrones a drama queen.

R. L.'s work relationships ranged from respectful but cautiously aloof disinterest, to respectful complete disinterest. In limited fashion, he participated in the small talk at work. He found the meaningless and frivolous chatter a bit tedious, but necessary to be part of the team. Here "team" seems to have been redefined to facilitate some corporate caricature of true teamwork, but he re-

spectfully kept these thoughts to himself. Usually
he spoke about books he happened to be reading.
Since most of his co-workers had not read a book
in months or years, unless the book he brought
into discussion had been made into a movie, there
wasn't much conversation forthcoming. He in-
tended it as such.

He was there to do a job and he gave that his
honest effort all the while refusing to get sucked
into trivial drama. On the whole, R. L. guessed
he was liked, but not well liked, not that he especially cared one way or another. Being liked or
not liked by his "teammates" never had been on
his very short list of things to care about. His
co-workers gave him his space, cubical 15, which
they allowed him as a personal sanctuary of sorts
and rarely intruded. That worked out just fine for
him. The workplace provided fertile ground and
ample opportunity to both exercise nihilism and
observe social—behavioral norms; he even had his
own space of sorts to do so, courtesy of XYZ.

He followed the rules and regulations for the
most part. Although R. L. fundamentally dis-

agreed with the human resource mentality that the entire workforce at XYZ represented a resource commodity, waiting to be fully mined, extracted, exploited, and sucked dry, after which time they could easily be replaced, he accepted this as reality. It was a competitive job market with dozens of eager prospective new employees just waiting to replace any previously eager but now spent worker bee, less than a drone, whose useful corporate life expectancy had been exceeded, thereby relegating said worker to the discard pile, the dung heap of no longer productive employees.

He derived no particular enjoyment, satisfaction, or sense of fulfillment from the sterile work of performing his accounts management functions. The work itself, nearly devoid of creative expression, was rather boring. R. L. refused to believe the *Myth of Sisyphus* as perpetrated by Camus, who wrote about the joy and fulfillment the tireless Grecian must have felt by endlessly performing his repetitive task. If R. L. cared, this reality might be disturbing or somehow unsettling. The notion that work should be enjoyable could become an attachment, an expectation of enjoyment could only lead to disappointment when enjoyment did not flow. Neither his identity nor his sense of enjoyment and fulfillment were defined by his work or work performance. He maintained a Buddhist nonattachment and thus kept free and untethered. He had read years ago that the Buddha was a nihilist.

R. L. diligently clocked in and out on time, and collected his biweekly paycheck, a straightforward example of the exchange of money for services that in reality did not differ much from prostitution. His condom protecting him from workplace transmitted disease was his adamant refusal to get sucked into the incessant drama that infected most of his colleagues.

Abstinence as a method to prevent burnout served him effectively as well. There were no gold watches for twenty-five years of devoted service. That he had made it for three years in itself was somehow remarkable; he even suspected that some of his fellow cubicons were beginning to follow his nonchalant lead in passionate disinterest and self-preservation. He suffered no delusions of grandeur at this imitation as a form of flattery. They were all there trying to survive. He must be doing something right to have made it this long.

Despite his best efforts, uncomfortable encounters, fraught with potential conflict, sometimes occurred. Today illustrated this *par excellence* when he went to pick up some documents waiting and finally executing through the print queue. The shared printer, positioned near the breakroom in little more than a cubby, stood sequestered off to a corner. It sometimes provided clandestine meeting space for non-approved workplace interactions. A former employee had been fired after his ass-print photocopy had somehow been duplicated and left in the document retrieval tray. Since each employee had to code entry their use of the copy machine, it didn't require Sherlock Holmes to figure out whodunit. Pretty asinine to his way of thinking.

Tanya had only started last month; thus far, R. L. sensed some confusion and consternation on her part in their here-to-date limited interactions. Why was he not beguiled? Why did he seem immune to her charms, her poise, and her pheromones of intense femininity? Why, thus far had R. L. not fallen under her bewitching spells so that she could devour him like a succubus? Was he gay, in a committed relationship, a complete and total loser that she should not even bother to expend effort upon? Her enquiring mind wanted to know. Now, the confines of the copy-room, where she stood in subtly perfumed arrogance, provided her with the perfect chance to get to the bottom of his apparent immunity. He stood cornered and trapped, wary of danger.

She grabbed his ID badge, a clear violation of his personal space, but he felt momentarily frozen. Bringing his picture up towards her face, she smiled deviously, then intoned:

"R. Leviticus...how come you don't put your whole first name?"

Undoubtedly, she knew his first name was "Rectum" and thought she saw an opening to confirm this oddity, maybe ask about how it was given to him, or some other coy and manipulative strategy to crack the mystery of his indifference towards her, to eat him up so she could spit him out later. Perhaps she thought to use this information to somehow demean him or belittle him or to gain some theoretical advantage. Perhaps all of the above.

His ID retracted back into position, similar to a retracting dog leash that she momentarily held in steady self-assured control. She nail-snapped his first initial, emblazoned on the nametag, with a French-manicured and decorated fingernail, a nail likely in violation of HR: 26, C., ii which regulated personal hygiene and appearance. A policy Dickhead would never enforce as he too had fallen under the vixen's spell, and, quite frankly, he appeared to be afraid of Tanya, or at least what she could do if reprimanded. Hell hath no fury...

Once, standing near the water cooler, R. L. overheard Mike and the boss pause in their football machismo-speak conversation and watch, or stare, or better yet, ogle as new employee Tanya passed them both and headed down the corridor. Rendered powerless and speechless, void in strength matching a head-shaved and totally bald Sampson, they gawked at the female gravitational wave drawing and sucking every bit of their consciousness as she wordlessly wiggled and strut her way to cubical 6.

"That girl can hurt you." Mike managed to gasp and give voice to their shared thought and desire.

Joseph Dickerson simply grunted a "Tell me about it..." As oxygen returned to the water cooler atmosphere upon Tanya's disappearance, they resumed their football-speak.

To R. L., she represented some sort of venomous, vituperative, vitriolic vixen. A shrew in sheep's clothing who typified so many women who had anger and attitude and used their feminine wiles in the worst possible ways. In the Dr. Phil, Men are from Mars, speed dating, match.com universe of relationships, Tanya was both a feminazi and an attention whore. To her, a man represented disposable packaging for her own sexual gratification or for spermatozoa when procreation became the agenda. Notwithstanding her attractiveness, his best strategy in dealing with this particular co-worker was strict avoidance.

Trapped as he was within the confines of the copy-room cubby, he could think of several retorts. Prior to responding to her question, his moment of reverie, while he collected his thoughts before answering, was misinterpreted as shame, as he remained frozen and trapped in Tanya's web. She probed further into the armor-chink of his momentary non-response.

"The 'R' doesn't have anything to do with the digestive track, does it?" Judging from the smirk on her face, which none-to-subtly suggested she knew she had him at that moment, he considered and chose his word carefully. His answer undoubtedly surprised her.

He considered suggesting that being adjacent to a "Rectum" certainly made her an asshole. Part of him wanted to punch her in liquid, floating, visualized turd-in-the-punchbowl refreshment. He thought of rolling up his sleeve and pointing to his "FYN" tattoo, but he opted for a different, more tactful and cerebral approach.

"Copernicus." That was it, a single word.

He handed her the document she had print-
ed out, taking pleasure in her look of confusion
and puzzlement. In his answer, he doubted she
would understand the reference to the enlightened
astronomer who both discovered and proved the
sun and entire Milky Way galaxy does not revolve
around the earth. In her introsexual, solipsistic,
Tabinda view of her emasculating self, he knew she
wouldn't get it. If she bothered to look up Copernicus, perhaps to make sure the astronomer's first
name was not "Rectum," or perhaps seeking clues
to why her particular color of kryptonite did not
work on this particular co-worker, he still felt sure
she wouldn't get it. Despite her outward physical beauty, despite her attitude that screamed, "I
got it going and I damn sure know it," despite
her cheerleading squad of pom-pom dancing sup-
porters shouting, "My team is HOT, your team
is NOT," despite all outward appearances, R. L.
knew his co-worker was a bit pneumocephalic, and
this particular girlfriend would never get it. After
all, she was emblematic of what so many of her

contemporaries valued. In the worthless currency she and those like her traded in, his answer had no value. He was not about to fawn upon Tanya; at best, he could tolerate what she represented. She could not understand that. That was okay, he answered not for her edification, but for his own personal pleasure.

Witnessing her baffled reaction to his response, he repeated, "Copernicus", and left. In the wake of her complete confuzzlement, with the word somehow echoing in the silence, R. L. had an eargasm. The entire exchange lasted less than a minute.

If you want to avoid workplace drama and have occasional eargasms, try the following:

Rectum's Survival Tips, Part Nine

- *Don't sell your soul to the company in exchange for a paycheck. Insulate yourself in the recognition that in the company's eyes you are expendable and replaceable. If you are committed to soul selling, at least trade for something fun. A Hula-Hoop is oodles more fun than a soul-sucking job. Stop by your local toy department after work today.*

- *Don't be deceived by people who act and believe as though their shit doesn't stink. It does. Invest in some high-quality nose plugs and room deodorizer.*

- *Ophidiophobia is advised. That's a good word to look up and impress your friends and family by dropping into casual conversation. Be wary of vipers and pythons who want to bite you and then squeeze out your life juice.*

- *Choose words carefully and measure their potency by how well they provoke the desired response. Of course, overdoing this can lead to smug satisfaction overload. A wise person, not to be confused with a wise guy, said, "It is better to remain silent and be thought a fool, than to open your mouth and remove all doubt." (or something to that effect)*

A Not Very Good Day

Loss and lost in the urban jungle

The day started quite ordinary enough. R. L.'s typical morning routine included cleanup, a bowl of oatmeal, and idle one-sided conversation with Mephisto, who basked in a patch of sunlight and occasionally blinked indifference. Dressed in his XYZ company attire, he walked to the subway and settled into the thirty-minute ride. Today, the typical retinue of work-weary travelers sent text messages, looked forward to the weekend––still two days away—snapped selfies, dozed, and avoided eye contact, all the while providing R. L. with endless fodder for observation and potential entertainment. He did get to witness a brief kerfuffle when a woman sat next to a tidy, prim-looking passenger and promptly sneezed. Instead of a polite, "Bless you," the following exchange occurred:

"You should cover your sneeze better. I hope you're not spreading germs."

"I think I'm allergic to your perfume."

"I'm not wearing any perfume."

"Well then, I must be allergic to you."

Some non-verbal snarls, growls, and grimaces followed until the woman sneezed a second time. De-escalation occurred when Ms. Prim changed her seat. R. L. could not help but note that no further sneezes ensued. He made a mental note that sneezing at will could be a useful social distancing skill. The remainder of the commute seemed mundane, although he and the Walker failed to connect in usual fashion. An omen perhaps?

At work, Mr. Dickerson behaved in ordinary Dickheadedness. Tanya had been released two weeks ago, and normalcy had returned to the office domain. The official reason for her dismissal might be in her HR file, but truthfully, during the first year of employment, any worker could be let go for no particular reason. R. L. had formulated his own speculation about her sudden departure, accompanied first by her tears, then by defiant yelling and swearing and, "Who the f#%k do you think you are, and who needs this f#%king piss-ant job anyway?" At that particular moment, Tanya, along with desk contents in a flimsy cardboard box, swaggered past R. L.'s cubical announcing loudly, while pointing her well-manicured fingers for emphasis, "You're all a bunch of losers!"

R. L. didn't take it personally. The pointing could have been directed at him but, quite frankly, he didn't care. The productivity reports clearly demonstrated a significant reduction in the collective office work effort since Tanya had been hired. Coincidence, statistical correlation, or causal, the boss, despite his shortcomings, could not deny reality. Sure enough, productivity two weeks later had statistically corrected to the norm. Was it fair? Probably not. Did R. L. care? Definitely not.

Work today did offer a more than usually boring mandatory in-service on a meaningless topic. R. L. had perfected a countenance of interest while allowing his mind to drift to nothing in particular. While he did acknowledge the disingenuous nature of appearing to be paying attention, he felt some weird satisfaction in shifting his attention to consider the overall implications of occupying time with a mind-numbingly inane in-service and actually being paid to sit there in feigned interest.

Another day, another dollar. He stopped at the library on the way home. Only two stations before his normal last stop, he planned to walk home and knew he would have some new reading material to delve into.

The library remained a bastion of righteousness to R. L.'s way of thinking––publicly funded, a resource for all to utilize freely, information sharing without ads or attempts to sell him something. His nihilistic inclinations had him caring little for most things, but this did not extend to the library and all it represented. The library was on his short list of things that he cared about. It was something sacred and worth fighting for, all the more so because of Mrs. Elkson's presence––the aged librarian, infinitely patient, a vast storehouse of knowledge, a true force of goodness. Her sole purpose in life, or so it seemed, was simply to help the patrons. That, and care for her progressively dementing husband. Over the years R. L. frequented the library, Mrs. Elkson and he had developed a friendship of sorts, founded upon a deep love of books.

"R. L., I put aside some new titles that I thought might appeal to you." A tear glistened in the corner of her eye and an unmistakably forlorn look removed all the usual smile creases. She sighed.

"Is everything okay Mrs. Elkson? Did something happen to Mr. Elkson?"

A distant look ensued; momentarily, she appeared to be in a far-off place. "Nothing that hasn't been happening for the last few years. Anyway, it doesn't much matter." She and her smile lines returned. "'You will never truly know yourself or the strength of your relationships until both have been tested by adversity.' Do you know who said that?"

File cards flipped in R. L.'s memory and a moment later he ventured, "J. K. Rowling...Surprisingly philosophical and inspirational, but not the sort of quote leaving me to think everything is fine. Mind if I ask what's going on?"

She slid the books toward him, sighed, and added rather matter-of-factly, "Haven't you read the sign?" As R. L. stood by clueless, she added, "It's been posted on the front door for two weeks." Still clueless. "After forty-three years. Oh well, all good things must come to an end."

He responded, "Chaucer," and she beamed.

"Are you leaving? Retiring? Please tell me that you haven't been fired."

"Heavens no, but I'm afraid my Frank can't be left home alone anymore and that means my tenure here is coming to a close. Tomorrow's my last day. They're having a little retirement party for me. Sign's been posted for two weeks."

Devastation!

"You'll be working I'm sure, so this is probably the last time I'll see you...That is unless you want to make a trip uptown to visit, come to book club, have tea? I've been wanting to introduce you to my neighbor a couple of doors down, a lovely girl, not quite the bibliophile you are, but I'm sure you can find something to talk about."

"Isn't there a children's book about 'A Terrible, Horrible, No Good, Very Bad Day'? I think my mother read it to me when I was a kid."

"'Alexander and the Terrible, Horrible, No Good, Very Bad Day' by Judith Viorst. It's a classic. We still use it for story time."

"Mrs. Elkson, I'm very sorry that I didn't notice the sign, but I am going to try and make your party tomorrow. You have been a beacon of light and a bastion of knowledge."

"That sounds like an original quote and you are kind to say so. I wish we had more people like you. Reading doesn't have the glamour it used to enjoy. I guess it isn't very sexy anymore, but then again, neither am I." She managed a tired smile. "*Excelsior!*"

R. L. leaned forward and gave her a big hug.

"*Excelsior!*" This, their closing exchange for years, rang hollow in his ears. Exiting, he noted the sign on the library's front door. The party was at 2: PM. Mr. Dickerson would need to make an exception.

He bought a dozen roses on the way home. He imagined Mrs. Elkson hadn't gotten flowers in a long time. Maybe he would stop by for tea some weekend. That thought cheered him a little, but that all changed the moment he got home.

Entering his apartment, it felt unusually cold. The broken window leading to the fire escape said it all. Robberies in the building weren't unusual and now he could just add his name to the crime victim statistics. A quick inventory revealed a missing toaster, blender, and gaming console. All portable enough but of little value in total. He called the police to report the break-in. He called the super who said he would replace the glass tomorrow. Tonight, R. L. should tape some newspaper or plastic over the broken window; he figured to do that after the police finished, in case they needed to take pictures, collect evidence, etc.

Ordinarily, he tried to avoid contact with law enforcement at all costs. But the officers were both professional and thorough. They confirmed R. L .'s speculation that the crime most likely represented scrounging for drug money. They seemed surprised at how little of value R. L. reported missing, but the benefit of a spartan and frugal lifestyle provided the only consolation for the robbery. The police told him he could pick up the police report at the precinct tomorrow. He would need it for an insurance claim.

He could replace the toaster at a secondhand store for less than $10.00. The blender had been stuck on low for two years and only chopped. It did look nice parked on his kitchen countertop as a decoration. He could replace his old console with a used old console. There probably wasn't enough to file a claim and the insurance company would be sure to raise his rates. He wasn't even sure why he had renter's insurance anyway.

He really didn't feel hungry but spooned some soup and reflected on the day. Then the earthquake-level devastation hit him, rocking his world. *Where's Mephisto?*

R. L. searched high and low, in every corner and crevice. He ran the dryer hoping Mephisto would be drawn to the heat and warmth, but all efforts to locate the gecko proved fruitless. It had been sunny earlier in the day. Had Mephisto escaped outside to bask in the sun? Was he lost and cold in the dark autumn night?

He grabbed a flashlight and climbed the fire escape searching in vain for his little buddy, calling his name, all to no avail.

R. L. plopped onto the couch in mounting grief and anxiety. Two things that he cared about, two of the only four things on his short list, both suffered losses on the same day. First the library, and now Mephisto. At moments such as these, the mind begins to play tricks. Maybe the gecko wanted to escape all along, wanted to explore the world beyond this ratty shithole of a place even with the steady cockroach-inspired cuisine. What if he had been kidnapped or rather petnapped? Would R. L. be getting a ransom note. He would gladly pay.

As these thoughts percolated, R. L. realized it might be a good idea to make some missing gecko posters with a picture of Mephisto and then he realized he didn't have any pictures of his housemate. "Rectum, you are an asshole!" He said it out loud for emphasis. It's not like he posted endless pet photos on Facebook or Instagram or imitated some angry cat meme of short videos by uploading go-go gecko videos. But, if Mephisto returned, R. L. promised himself he would take some pictures of the endlessly smiling lizard. *Probably still smiling even if he's cold and tired, and lonely and hungry*, he thought to himself.

He glanced at the bouquet of roses and spoke to no one; not even Mephisto was around to hear. "This has been a terrible, horrible, no good, very bad day!" Three cockroaches scurried past. He sighed, "*Excelsior...*"

As you ponder your forlorn existence in the nighttime of your soul, remember:

Rectum's Survival Tips, Part Ten

- *Sometimes you're the feline and sometimes you're the litterbox.*

- *Sleep is a great comforter when you feel tired and miserable. Wake up the next day and feel refreshed and miserable. Repeat this wash-spin-rinse-spin cycle until you are too dizzy to remember why you were feeling miserable to begin with.*

- *If you can invent magic tape that repairs a broken heart as easily as masking tape mends broken glass, you can probably be featured on Shark Tank.*

- *If you are too serious about life you shouldn't be reading this book, but since you are reading this book, you can genuinely realize you needn't take life so seriously. Feel better now?*

HANGING OUT WITH FRIENDS

Friends, football, and paranormal fantasies

It turned out his boss wasn't such a Dickhead after all. R. L. explained the situation, got a reminder on the correct procedure to follow, as detailed in policy HR: 61, subsection M, part iv, and the proper forms to complete. Since the request was being filed late, he would make an exception under the circumstances in exchange for

R. L. agreeing to work the day after Thanksgiving, normally a difficult day to staff. That presented no problem at all since R. L. never participated in all the hullabaloo around Black Friday, once-in-a-lifetime sales, and overhyped holiday shopping fever that gripped society.

Now, R. L. enjoyed an early start to the weekend with a free afternoon and a bouquet of roses to deliver. Bittersweet. The send-off for Mrs. Elkson had the usual fare of memorable stories shared by colleagues, laudatory remarks about the guest of honor, comments about dedication, pleasure to work with, will be missed, wishing luck for the future, tears and hugs. R. L. listened intently and was genuinely moved by the show of gratitude. Few patrons attended, but that didn't surprise him. Cake and coffee and mingling followed. R. L. mostly watched from the edges, glad to see the outpouring of respect and glad that he could attend. Mrs. Elkson got all choked up when she greeted him, thanking him for attending, thanking him for the flowers, thanking him for supporting the library and all it stood for.

"You've got it backwards, Mrs. Elkson. I should be thanking you." He gave her a long hug, ignoring the tears welling in his eyes, and promised he would stop by for tea.

She perked up for a moment, grabbed his hand and crossed the room. "I want to introduce you to the new librarian." She stopped and beamed effusively. "R. L., this is Bethany, the new librarian. Bethany, this is R. L., one of our staunchest patrons and one of the few regulars."

Standing in front of him with outstretched hand, the new librarian surprised him. She couldn't be more than late twenties.

"Hi, Arl, I'm Bethany. Mrs. Elkson sure is leaving big shoes to fill." She gestured around the room, then pointed to her feet. I'm only a size six and a half, so I'm going to have to really work hard." She smiled.

Very pleasant and kinda spunky, R. L. thought.

"You're funny, Bethany. You'll do fine." With hand curled over her mouth, Mrs. Elkson leaned to Bethany's ear and in a hushed conspirator-whisper confided, "I'm only a size seven." She straightened.

"By the way, It's 'R. L.' not 'Arl' like Carl without the 'C'.

"You mean like C. S. Lewis, or T. S. Elliot, or D. H. Lawrence, or H. G. Wells?"

"Actually, it's just R. L., the initials for my first and last names," he said.

Her cell phone chimed. "Excuse me...I have to take this."

She returned a moment later. "I am so sorry, Mrs. Elkson, that's the pet shelter where I volunteer. Someone went home sick. They're desperate, so I'm going to have to get going. I'm sure I'll be calling you for your advice." She looked around, "They really love and appreciate you here. I think this is going to be the best job I ever had." She turned and extended her hand. "Nice to meet you R. L.; you look like an Arl to me. Hope to see you around."

After Bethany's exit, he spoke to Mrs. Elkson. "She's not quite what I expected. The librarian stereotype is a bit more reserved. She's a bottle of sunshine with the lid uncorked—very bright, full of life, and not lacking in enthusiasm for sure."

She replied, "Knowledge is power, but enthusiasm pulls the switch."

"You got me there. I don't know the author of that quote."

"I looked it up once, but the authorship is uncertain. So much about life is uncertain…"

***

He and Andy had known one another since high school. Apart from being recognized by fellow classmates with the "There is nothing outstanding about me award," a well-deserved honor, especially since there were so many competing student candidates, Andy was the only classmate who recognized the profound contradiction of being outstandingly non-outstanding. Additionally, he fully embraced the nickname referencing this, "Ono", as a private joke between the two of them. He also shared R. L.'s nihilistic impulses. Well, at least he used to.

Ever since getting married seven years ago, his high school buddy had been creeping towards "normalcy", a term used with a modicum of disdain to describe the aberrant attachment to pedestrian values. It had started slowly, much like continental drift. However, R. L. had astutely noticed that since the birth of Andy's daughter four years ago, the incessant drift had accelerated. Switching metaphors, he silently and sadly opined that his friend's conversion to mainstream thinking had started as a drip, but left unattended, the drip had become a trickle, and would likely progress relentlessly to a torrent. Not surprisingly, Andy clutched a bottle of lite beer, a sure sign that he neared the precipice of irrevocable conversion to the dark side of meaninglessness––the overpopulated side where masses yearning to be free did not realize they had voluntarily enslaved themselves. Fortunately, Andy had come tonight without his wife, who normally prowled close to her spouse and snarled protectively whenever she saw R. L., whose influence upon her husband she conspicuously disapproved of.

"Hey Ono, no ball and chain tonight; how did you manage that?"

"Babysitter got sick. Marianne said it would be okay for me to come, but I can only stay an hour or so."

"Can I buy you a beer?"

Andy looked at his hand, still holding a lite beer, and cringed with the full impact of R. L.'s offer. "Damn! You don't miss a trick." A big grin followed as he placed the half-empty bottle on a table with a decisive thud. "I'm done drinking this metaphorical Kool-Aide. C'mon, I'll buy us both some real beer and we can relive the glory days of precious youth. I'm not dead yet!"

As they made their way to the bar, R. L. did recall with a certain sense of reassurance that the glacial creep of the ice age eventually stopped, and the ice then began to recede. Perhaps hope remained.

"How's everything at home?"

"Could be better. Things used to be a lot better when I just didn't care. Marianne almost has me convinced we should buy a minivan. I look at you and realize how carefree you are. I'm sure you don't get weighed down thinking about what kind of car to buy. I think to myself, 'Hell, I used to be that way.'"

"I'm both asking and telling you this as a friend, why do you put the blame on her?" Since Andy just stood there with a bit of a surprised look, R. L. continued. "Who cares what kind of car you drive as long as it gets you where you want to go? Does it really make a difference?"

"When you put it that way..."

"Happy wife...happy life."

"You know, I don't know why she doesn't like you. You make a lot of sense and help keep me grounded. I really shouldn't give two shits whether we drive around in a minivan or a friggin' hearse for that matter."

"Now that's the Ono I remember talking. Dude, I was afraid you were headed down the path of endless worry and consumption." With that, they broke into a familiar chorus of, *The Big Rock Candy Mountain*. Singing that Hobo song felt good, and the two friends philosophized and laughed as they nostalgically recalled some old antics when the world seemed less complicated.

"Gotta split, man. Can't wait to tell Marianne you persuaded me to go with the minivan. I'm gonna let her pick out the color too because I don't care one lousy bit about the color. I'll bet she thinks I'm drunk, but I'm not. What I am is sure glad I came and we had the chance to revisit what's important. Conclusion—not much. Damn, R. L. I'm gonna sleep good tonight." They parted after embracing, both feeling the unmatched upbeatness of male bonding.

Since they had parked themselves off in a corner, R. L. made his way to the middle of the room. He waved a greeting to an acquaintance and looked to find the restroom. That's when he spotted her. He harbored no secrets to himself that he hoped Vanessa would be here. Seeing her long auburn curls, he could almost smell the freshness of her beauty from a distance. She sat among a group of girlfriends chatting and laughing. Behind them, five or six guys were transfixed in front of six TV screens playing an assortment of football games and a single golf match. He ambled over and stood close by his friend, patiently listening to bits of their conversation. He overheard, "Juicy," "Steaming hunk," "Can you believe it?" and "No way, girlfriend," and gathered from these and other snippets that they were discussing the latest Danielle Steele wannabe romance novel.

En masse, they paused as the group of sports enthusiasts yelled with expletives about a bad call. That's when Vanessa spied him and introduced him as her friend.

"R. L., this is Julie, Trish, and Roxanne." She pointed them out. He wanted to say to the last friend that she could call him Cyrano but thought better. Given the literature they were discussing, referring to the famous love triangle depicted in Edmond Rostand's play would not likely be recognized.

"Please, don't let me interrupt your book club."

Vanessa continued. "He is quite the reader, spends way too much time in the library," eyes rolled, "and needs to get out more instead of hanging out with Doosguyevski."

R. L. cringed.

"I think you mean, Dostoyevsky." Roxanne came to the rescue. "We were discussing a romance novel. I don't imagine that's the kind of stuff you read."

"Ahem, as a matter of fact, I recently finished..." and he spouted off the title of the paranormal romance he had recently completed.

Trish gasped. "Really? You are talking about the story with the vangel and the buxom cook on the dude ranch. Wasn't it awesome? Did you read the other books in the series?"

A sudden discomfort gripped him as he found himself the center of attention with rapt women hanging onto every word he said. Vanessa had a curious look of skepticism, or was it admiration, or just what the hell was it? Trish batted her eyes waiting for his response.

He nodded. "Yes, that's the one. No, I haven't read any of the others."

No one said anything, but the open-jawed looks on their faces nonverbally communicated they were stunned, or was it awe? At this moment,

being the center of attention among a cohort of
attractive women, his center of gravity shifted into
parts unknown, but only slightly south of his belt
buckle. He added, "Are they any good?"

Trish responded enthusiastically, "Oh yeah, definitely. I don't want to give them away, but you
should read them. Actually," she glanced around
to the others, "we don't know any guys who read
these kinds of books." Heads nodded in agreement. A cheer rose from the football fanatics and
she pointed to the men. "They are too gobs-
macked with football." Another cheer followed at
the replay.

"Aren't they...the books...aren't they all kind of
the same?"

As a group, they burst out laughing and simultaneously pointed to the TV screens. "Aren't they
all the same?"

R. L. reeled in confusion, but Vanessa spotted it
immediately and helped him out.

She pointed. "You see that football, that's their
entertainment. This," she reached into her bag and
pulled out the romance novel under discussion

previously, "is ours." The group then began to simultaneously explain it to him. They so much wanted him to understand that it was not simple brain numbing nonsense.

Julie summed it up in a cross-gender epiphany of Men from Mars having new insight into Women from Venus. "It's escapism, pure and simple."

Still reeling, still trying to wrap his head around this revelation, R. L. asked naively, "What are you escaping from?"

This provoked another outburst of laughter. "Everything! Our boring jobs, mundane lives..." they each seemed to be shouting out different personal realities..."lack of true romance, sexual dissatisfaction..." This last comment came from Trish who seemed to be staring at him longingly. R. L. thought Vanessa blushed.

"I get it...I get it. Escape from modern life, inconsequential relationships, meaningless work, the total banality of existence. Ladies, I can't express how grateful I am for these insights!"

"Finally!" An exasperated sigh from Roxanne, "Somebody understands us!"

A loud "Boo" and gestures of disgust, as the main game of interest ended with the home team losing. As R. L. and the four women watched, a broad-shouldered man in the group with long blonde hair stood, his back to them.

"Okay, okay, so I lost ze bet." He took empty beer cans in each hand and crushed them flat against the side of his head. His buddies all cheered.

"You see," Vanessa spoke quietly, "they have their entertainment, and we have ours."

With that, the group of men headed over to join the women. The two groups were paired! Surprise morphed into a feeling of male inadequacy as R. L. realized his circumstance of the moment—he sat as the single male talking paranormal romance. Suddenly, he flashed a vision of himself in a sewing class repairing football jerseys for the winning team. No, worse...he panicked and imagined himself trying to breastfeed an infant as the real men prepared to go out and hunt for food.

Battling these feelings of pathetic masculine inadequacy, he almost lost it when beer-can-brain put his arm around Vanessa. He looked like the cover of a romance novel—strong angular chin, rippling muscles, undisguised six-pack beneath a tight shirt revealing his manly chest. Apart from faint red circular impressions on each temple, he looked like a Viking chieftain with perfect teeth. And he had his arm around Vanessa! Complete vertigo...

"R. L., this is my boyfriend, Dolfe. Dolfe, this is my friend, R. L."

A grunt ensued followed by an extended hand that R. L. made the mistake of grasping. He winced at the strength of the grip, but the pain brought him back to reality. The rest of the group had paired off and seemed to be getting ready to leave. Trish dropped something in his pocket.

"So, Dolfe, where are you from, Valhalla? Can I buy you a mead?" It was clear he made neither connection.

"He's from Denmark." Vanessa glared. "And I think we should probably get going."

R. L. suddenly remembered this all started en route to the restroom and now his bladder screamed for mercy. "Speaking of which, I need to go too, but I mean..." he pointed to the men's room.

"Yah, me too." That came from Dolfe, who did look to be a little drunk.

R. L. led the way and the great Dane followed.

As the two men both relieved themselves, R. L. realized they weren't all that different. They both pissed in a urinal and there was some strange comfort in having that in common. He felt relieved in more than one way.

Reconnecting with Vanessa, Dolfe put his arm around R. L. "You have some good friends, Vanessa." The man embrace that followed was not all that different from how he parted with Andy.

Life could be worse. Bested by a Nordic demigod in a quest to claim the most beautiful woman in the village--it had been this way for centuries. R. L. had the smart genes and Dolt, that is, Dolfe, got the manly ones.

Finding Trish's phone number in his pocket reminded him of something one of his high school teachers once said, "A man isn't someone who simply teases the hair on his chest." And if you want to avoid chest hair braiding and get phone numbers placed in your pocket, read on:

Rectum's Survival Tips, Part Eleven

- *Henry Ford reportedly said, "You can have whatever color car you want as long as it's black." This will make more sense after you crush some beer cans against the side of your head.*

- *Relationships can be incomprehensibly confusing until you realize, at some level, people are all the same, they just have different heads.*

- *Don't discount paranormal romance as complete vapid nonsense fill. Appreciate the entertainment and pure escapist es-*

sential nature of this literary form. How we each choose to escape the complete vapid nonsense of monotonous reality is just a matter of personal preference.

- *Respect gender diversity even if you don't have a clue what it's all about.*

- *Whether you pee with the toilet seat up or down says little about who you really are.*

WEIRD STUFF

[This space intentionally left blank]

Things felt out of balance with some weird things going on of late. R. L. wondered if there might be some kind of celestial realignment happening, a harmonic coherence or quite possibly a discordant chaos, a dissonance on a cosmic scale. Were recent events in his life something unilaterally affecting the arc of his karma or was there a more universal reconfiguration at play? Does the universe play with itself? His thoughts meandered as he manipulated chopsticks.

He reserved Chinese takeout for special occasions when he needed to think. Chopsticks, fung chow, and jasmine tea had a unique thought-focusing quality amenable to new insights and seeing patterns that were otherwise hidden.

News of late regurgitated the same recurrent litany of divisive politics, world tensions, climate challenges, people with their hair on fire over trivial matters, pundits, parodies, and the usual flotsam and jetsam floating about. Perhaps the universe had had enough and this was indeed the beginning of the great purge, the long-awaited shift of humanity into a more spiritually enlightened *Homo Sapiens 2.0.* Unlikely, he thought as he deposited some rice noodles into his mouth. It all appears to be same old, same old.

On the surface, nothing weird seemed to be occurring. He dug deeper: deep state, dark matter, God particle, quantum distortion, black hole, Holy Ghost, spirits, ethereal beings, astral projection, out of body, out of mind. No hits on that particular stream of consciousness.

He started another: UFOs, alien abduction, cosmic disclosure...That's really odd! He sipped some tea and concentrated. His stream of consciousness abruptly stopped at cosmic disclosure. Try as he might, R. L. could not connect another thought. He shook his head in bewilderment until gradually he understood. As a wide grin erupted, the head shaking became head nodding in comprehension.

He started this inquiry wondering if the universe planned some realignment. It ended right back where it started with a thought-stopping "cosmic disclosure." Like a beautiful ouroboros, a snake devouring its own tail in a circle of cosmic harmony, he reached a conclusion. Yes, the universe does play with itself or at least with him. He began to clean up.

The particular circumstances of weird stuff in his own life was all the universe at the microcosmic scale having fun. Mr. Dickerson had called him unexpectedly into his office on Tuesday. R. L. prepared himself for some R & R; instead, he got the following.

"Rectum, I have a proposal I would like to run by you to see if you are up for it."

"Yes, sir. What is it you would like to propose?"

"You know everyone here in the office likes you, they look up to you." He looked at R. L. expecting some response.

"That is appreciated, sir, but I am the tallest person in the office, and I think it's more accurate to say no one dislikes me. It's more of a double negative if you see what I mean. I try to get along with everyone and just do my work."

"Exactly. You're studious and reliably consistent, don't get ruffled too easily. People respect that and I want you to know that I have noticed."

"Thank you, sir. Is that all?"

"No. I'm going to Dallas in early December for a week-long training retreat the company is sponsoring. Normally corporate would send a temporary replacement, but most of the managers will be at the seminar. I would like to put you in charge while I'm gone. How does that sound to you?"

"Well..."

"Ms. Lederman in Philadelphia will be available for emergency backup. Corporate wants all of the attendees to disconnect from technology on this training. It's more of a roughing it team-building affair than sit down workshops. I'll leave you the number for the hotel where you can reach me at night if it's absolutely necessary. But I don't see that as likely. I wouldn't ask if I didn't think you can handle it. I think you're future management; consider this as a dry run. What do you say?"

"Thank you, sir, I'll do my best."

"Oh," Mr. Dickerson looked down at his shoes a moment. "There's no additional compensation for this, but I will put a solid entry into your HR file."

R. L. thought a moment. In retrospect, maybe he should have just remained quiet, but the surprise at this turn of events momentarily checked his restraint. "That's not necessary, Mr. Dickerson. I'm doing it because you requested, not as a *quid pro quo.*"

His boss looked completely perplexed by that
answer and R. L. saw facial muscles tighten. What
went through his boss's mind in that final exchange hung like a piece of dangling chad in one
of those instantaneous moments that seems to be
never ending. R. L. was dismissed with a thank you
grunt.

Now Thursday, his interactions with his boss
had subsequently been minimal and all were accompanied by a facial expression of confused bewilderment.

***

More cosmic peculiarities intruded upon the nor-
mality and consistency of his routines. Following
up on a text message from the library informing
him that the interlibrary loan book he requested
on Cortés, the Spanish Conquistador, had arrived,
he stopped there at the end of the day.

Bethany smiled when she saw him. "Hey Arl, I see you got my text." She slid over a small pile of four books.

"Thanks, Bethany! I recognize the one I requested, what are these other three?"

"I reviewed the profile of books you've borrowed and I thought you would like this." She held up a copy of *First Love*, by Ivan Turgenev. "I minored in Russian Lit and saw you had read quite a few books by Tolstoy, Dostoevsky, and Solzhenitsyn. Turgenev doesn't get the recognition he deserves."

"Uhh...thanks...that's very thoughtful. What did you major in?"

"I had a second minor in English Lit, but I majored in Occidental Mythology."

"You mean like Greece, Rome, and the stuff Joseph Campbell writes about?" R. L. 's brows shot up as Bethany revealed these facts about herself. "How did you wind up here?"

"The inside joke is jobs in mythology are a myth." A sheepish smile preceded a shrug, "I did some teaching at the high school level. Most students aren't interested in reading literature these days, so it felt like there was too much resistance to sharing what I love."

"What's that?"

"Reading, exploring ideas," she gestured outward to the shelves of books. "There are endless worlds of possibility to explore and share."

Bethany's enthusiasm infected him. Was this an invitation to explore together? Certainly the interesting title to the Turgenev selection could be interpreted suggestively. Someone who liked to read––how novel! The marriage of novel as "new" and novel as "book" had cosmic overtones.

"How about the other books?"

She held up Immanuel Kant's *Critique of Pure Reason.* "It's a bit dense, and it's a real tome, but I think you'd be up to it."

"No need," he slid the book back towards the librarian. I have a used copy. It's on my shelf at home. It would be fun to discuss sometime."

"I'd like that, Arl." She smiled. "Mrs. Elkson said you're pretty interesting. I don't meet many bibliophiles. I'm at the pet shelter Tuesdays and Thursdays but am otherwise free."

"Speaking of the shelter, have you had any recent geckos show up? Mine went missing recently and I'm pretty bummed about it."

"Nope, we don't get many reptiles beyond an occasional snake and iguana. I can check with the other shelters in town if you like."

"Yeah, that would be great! How about this last book?"

"*Sentient:* science fiction...I'm big on sci fi, strange new worlds to explore, lots of interesting extrapolations and conjecture into human behavior. You know what they say, 'If you want to know the future of tomorrow, read sci fi today.' It seemed to me based on your profile that you were deficient in this genre."

"What's special about this book?"

"Obscure author, interesting ideas about telepathy and collective consciousness. Misfits and outcasts save the world. I think you would enjoy it. It would be fun to discuss." She slipped a piece of paper into the book and handed it over.

"U h m m ... y e a h ... a h h h ... s u r e ... a n d thanks...thanks a lot!"

The desk phone rang and the librarian broke away to answer while motioning with pinky and thumb to her free ear. "Call me."

R. L. disliked that particular call-me gesture, but at the moment he felt grateful for a reprieve to process what just had occurred unexpectedly and out of the blue. He waved goodbye. He rarely got flummoxed to the point of dumbfounded speech but Bethany completely confuzzled and tongue-tied him at that moment. In retrospect, he imagined his look of bewilderment must have rivaled Mr. Dickerson's. Misfits and outcasts––how had she so easily pegged him? What exactly is in his library profile?

He had a short list of things he cared about and a similarly short list of things that bothered him. While nihilism demanded a detached non-judgmental approach, the whole notion of profiles felt wrong to him. A psychographic profile based on your Facebook and other social media activity, a shopping and purchasing profile based on your shopping and purchasing activity on Amazon and elsewhere, a Google meta-profile based on everything you did on the internet––yikes! Scary stuff to his way of thinking and it just seemed somehow wrong and dehumanizing to classify people in such a way and then try to manipulate them by ads, pop ups, and "helpful" suggestions.

Worst of all––matchmaking profiles and dating apps. The proliferation of sites and services like eHarmony, Match.com, ChristianMingle, Tinder, Bumble, Zoosk and a panoply of others troubled him. The concept itself was fine as illustrated by what happened earlier with Bethany. They both enjoyed books and reading and that could be part of a profile that could help them to "discover" each other. The problem was rampant misrepresentation in creating profiles. People too easily create idealized versions of themselves and the algorithms don't know that. He refused to play that game of deception, but he softened as he realized there is a lot of deception and misrepresentation throughout society.

***

He sighed because he missed Mephisto. As he washed the dishes, his reptilian housemate would often perch on the wall over the sink and watch. At moments such as these, the lizard's etched-in-face eternal grin conveyed both understanding and be-musement. In silent communication of deep wis-dom, Mephisto would remind him thus: the world is a stage, dear Rectum Leviticus. Trust me. My kind have been around for millions of years com-pared to mere thousands of years for your kind. All of this is ephemeral and shall pass to dust. Play your part and watch the unfolding world with amusement. Care or not care, I smile along with the universe and so should you.

When weird things happen, here's what to do:

Rectum's Survival Tips, Part Twelve

- *If a lizard can evoke Shakespeare, and*

their brains are much smaller than yours, so can you. Google Shakespearian quotes and start practicing.

- *The universe is messin' with your head. Play along by stretching your arms wide and singing a silly song. If that doesn't make you feel better, clean your navel lint which should help to cleanse your navel center (dan t'ian) and improve the flow of chi connecting you to universal energy. After your cleansing and rebalancing, stretch your arms wide and sing a silly song. How do you feel now?*

- *Examine your personal profiles and draw conclusions about yourself, then feel buoyed and cheered in the recognition that you are not your profile.*

- *Be entirely subversive by Googling all sorts of strange and weird things to completely confuse their algorithms. When pop up ads for psychiatric services begin to display, re-*

turn your search activity to normal.

- *Adopt a new mantra to repeat through-out the day--weird is good, weird is good, weird is good. State this loudly and repeat-edly on a first date and see how much fun you have.*

A Family Gathering

Giving thanks for food, family, and fun

Every year, his family gathered at his parents' home in Westchester for Thanksgiving dinner. The continuity and consistency of this family tradition had the heartwarming attraction of watching reruns of a sit-com with new commercials to provide extra entertainment. This year, R. L. planned some auto-amusement by playing two different games he contrived.

The first involved bingo cards for each of the four other family members: his father, Walter; mother, Theresa; sister, Sally; and brother-in-law, Quinn. He had mentally prepared five individualized idiosyncratic winning categories for each. His name for this game: Family Unique Bingo or FUB for short.

Walter card––score 1 for each:

- Complain that he deserved a raise

- Complain that his children should visit more often

- Complain that he had no grandchildren

- Be a self-proclaimed expert in no less than 4 ways

- Have a new word of the day mentioned at least 5 times

Theresa's card–– score 1 for each:

- Would make three-bean casserole and claim it was R. L.'s favorite (it was not)

- Overcook the turkey

- Make a joke that only she finds funny

- Extol the virtues of Danny DeVito

- Mention Danny DeVito at least 6 times

Sally's card–– score 1 for each:
- Talk about her efforts to lose weight (despite not needing to)

- Make plans for plastic surgery

- Refuse to talk about work

- Discuss her latest home decorating ideas

- Celebrity gossip

Quinn's card–– score 1 for each:
- Endlessly talk about work

- Give unsolicited financial advice

- Argue with Walter

- Argue with Theresa

• Argue with Sally

R. L. devised a second game, developed as a new strategy to enhance his Thanksgiving: he would respond on a least a dozen occasions by saying, "Whatever floats your boat."

He took the subway to uptown Manhattan where his sister lived, and they drove in Quinn's BMW 750i luxury sedan. His brother-in-law discussed at length the merits of leasing by providing all sorts of irrelevant information about how to negotiate a car lease, all the while oblivious to R. L.'s repeated statements about having no desire to own or lease a car. He argued with R. L. that 'BMW" stood for 'British Motor Works' even though the cars were made in Germany, but R. L. pointed out it stood for *Bayerische Motoren Werke*, which referred to Bavaria. R. L. had no idea why he knew this because he truly didn't care. Quinn insisted that Bavaria was part of Austria not Germany, and the conversation ended when R. L. said, "Whatever floats your boat." He was well into completing Quinn's bingo card and they were only ten minutes into their commute.

"How's work?" Sally asked. She seemed pleased that R. L.'s boss has asked him to be in charge for a week. Quinn interjected that R. L. should have negotiated a raise or a better office or some other perk. He talked for a while about how well he was doing with his own work at J. P. Morgan.

After tuning out for all the self-aggrandizement and narcissistic me-me-me from Quinn, he asked his sister. "How's your work?"

"I don't want to talk about it."

"What do you want to talk about?"

There followed an almost predictable stream of solipsistic details about her new fad and fascination, the fabulous strawberries and cream diet, recommended by three different celebrities R. L. had never heard of. Then followed exhaustive details about her yoga classes, her studious adherence to a Pelaton exercise routine, her Fitbit statistics, her gluten sensitivity (did he know [three other unrecognized celebrities] also had gluten sensitivity?), why her particular blood type made it difficult to lose weight, and how she planned to have a boob job, a nose job––Quinn argued with her about the need for that as he thought her nose needed no improvement––and some non-surgical leg sculpting.

R. L.'s opinion, which he stated: "I think you look great, sis! Why do you want any of that?"

She beamed, "Thanks to my darling husband, I can afford to."

"Whatever floats your boat..."

Sally went on to discuss the new curtains, the new couch, the new rugs, the new lamps and how she was now a preferred customer at Wayfair. She sounded like a commercial. By the time they arrived, Sally's FUB card had been completed. There is something satisfying about predicting the predictable, much like the comfort of the familiar.

Upon entering his parents' home, R. L. handed over his Thanksgiving offering to his mother, the cook: a jumbo-sized bag of Jolly Ranchers.

"You are so sweet! You know that those are my favorite, and just so you know, I made your favorite three-bean casserole. I know how much you love that!"

Punch out the "B" on Theresa's card. He smiled, "Thanks, Mom, Thanksgiving wouldn't be the same without it."

"How was the traffic?" Walter asked Quinn. "The experts on the news are always saying how bad Thanksgiving traffic is, but I don't think it's as formidable a problem as they state." He mispronounced the accent on formidable as forMIDable. Quinn pointed out that as long as he had been a member of the family, Walter had never braved the Thanksgiving traffic; soon, they were arguing with one another.

R. L. felt elated at the steady and early progress of FUB. Theresa announced that dinner was ready, and they sat down.

Walter said family grace and in the midst of expressing thanks and gratitude he mentioned that he would be even more grateful if the higher ups where he worked would finally express their own thanks by giving him a raise. That seemed a little twisted.

During the meal, his father, in typical over-opinionated fashion, claimed that weather forecasters didn't have a clue about predicting the weather and while acknowledging that such forecasting represented a forMIDable challenge, his joints responded to barometric pressure, and by combining the number of times he got up to urinate the night before with the level of joint pain he felt after breakfast he could predict more accurately what the weather would be like.

A spirited but inappropriate meal time conversation about turmeric and other health supplements, spearheaded by Sally, quickly segued into discussion about nocturnal urination, prostate health, male supplements and claims from Walter that he knew more about this than anyone, and that a combination of garlic and ginger represented the panacea for both joint and prostate health and pretty much everything else except baldness. Non-surgical hair growth methods led to an argument culminating with R. L.'s statement to each of his family members as a group. "Listen everyone, whatever floats your boat. Hair replacement isn't important." He counted this scoring four times in his secondary game quite simply because he could.

Predictably, the turkey was overcooked in spite of Theresa following the "How to cook a perfect turkey" recipe in her new *Danny DeVito in the Kitchen Cookbook*. Predictably this launched a celebrity gossip discussion and an argument between Theresa and Quinn about why Danny DeVito should have received an Academy Award for his portrayal of the Penguin villain in the Batman remake which, Quinn argued, was even worse that the old TV series that he binge-watched during a snowstorm. "Holy Batman," he intoned like the Robin sidekick, "are you out of your mind, Mom, Danny DeVito isn't all you make him out to be."

"Well, I'm no Mother Theresa either." She began laughing at her comment that she apparently found funny. Score another mark on her card.

Walter came to his wife's rescue by changing the subject. "Your mother-in-law sure makes a forMI-Dable gravy."

There is was again, forMIDable, the obvious word of the day. A moment of awkward processing occurred as Dad poured a generous portion of gravy into the little well he had excavated into his mound of mashed potatoes. No one was quite sure whether to respond at all, and Theresa was oblivious and somehow still chuckling at her own humor despite a mouth full of a less-than-tender morsel of well-done turkey. His mother exhibited something akin to a vacuum-sealed vacuum––nothing got in and nothing got out because there was nothing inside trying to get out to begin with. R. L. had an insight at that moment about his own ability to tune the world out and be lost in auto-amusement. Perhaps he took after his mother more than he realized.

Dad broke the silence by half muttering, half exclaiming: "Yes, this sure is forMIDable." He forked some gravy-laden potatoes into his mouth and uttered an expression of yummified delight.

Sally, in some regressive role-playing to please Daddy, except she was not aware that she had regressed during the family celebrations, and under the slight impairment of alcoholic balm, piped in, "Yes indeed, it certainly is forMIDable. Can you pass it back my way?"

As Dad obliged, R. L. and Quinn locked eyes in momentary disbelief and chagrin at Sally. They both saw what just occurred. It wasn't that no one would ordinarily use that adjective to describe sauce or gravy, not even on an overhyped cooking show. It wasn't even the mispronounced emphasis on the second syllable. In the exchanged gaze of brother and brother-in-law was the tacit agreement and acknowledgement of, "Did you just hear what happened and can you believe Sally just regressed and said what she said?" moment of shared disbelief. Following this they exchanged a subtle head shake.

In that moment, the vast gulf of differences disappeared, whether those differences were materialistic, political, ideological, or any number of areas where R. L. and Quinn disagreed, their separation by a cavernous divide had ceased momentarily. In a split-second of détente, a unity-bonding-kumbaya moment of witness to unanimous agreement, the two men shared common ground. This unspoken solidarity, between them alone, nullified Sally's regressive behavior as the two men shared a head nod of mutual understanding.

Mom's loud chewing ended with a gulp of water followed by a soft belch; the sounds all amplified in the silence of the moment.

As though seemingly hearing and responding to her husband's comments in a slow-off-the-starting-blocks way, an interminably long synaptic delay slowing neuronal transmission, she cheerily said, "Thank you, Walter! It's a recipe from my *Danny DeVito's Favorites Cookbook*— that's his previous one. The secret is the added corn starch."

Hearing his father complain about something he didn't even have on Walter's bingo card, R. L. grew serious and asked. "Dad, why do you let that stuff bother you? What happened to the free-spirited couple you and Mom were when hitchhiking in California, when she was pregnant with me? What happened?"

"I'll tell you what happened: life...responsibili-ty...you...Sally...a job...a house...work. You know, life is hard."

"It's as hard as you make it. You need to lighten up. You're going to be dead a long time. Maybe you and Mom should plan a trip to California; have some fun."

"We could visit Danny DeVito's footprints on Hollywood Boulevard." Theresa looked hopeful.

"You don't understand. I'm not as young and foolish as I used to be. Let's not talk about it."

"Whatever floats your boat, Dad. I just think you should consider it."

In the lull between dinner and dessert, the "no grandchildren yet" conversation happened. All re-maining FUB categories were completed except one on Walter's card, as well as all the WFYB (Whatever floats your boat) retorts.

"I hope you don't hit any traffic on the way home, Quinn. R. L. it's too bad you have to work tomorrow. At least they give us a day off at work. I'd prefer a raise. After all I've given that company,

I certainly deserve it. Sally, enjoy the Black Friday sales."

"Theresa, sorry I argued with you so much about Danny DeVito, I know you adore him."

"I adore you too, Quinn. Thanks for coming!" She gave him a hug and a kiss.

As Walter escorted them to the car, he remarked, "You kids really should visit more often." BIN-GO!

There is true comfort in predictability and consistency and continuity––all essential ingredients to family traditions.

If you too want to learn the secrets of putting rich gravy on your mashed potatoes, read on:

Rectum's Survival Tips, Part Thirteen

- *If you think bingo is a game for senior citizens, you are missing out. Best to read this chapter again and plan for great fun at your next family gathering.*

- *B-I-N-G-O is a counting song for kids that involves clapping your hands. If you sing it and clap your hands you will feel childish. There are times when feeling childish is just what the moment calls for. Sing B-I-N-G-O and clap your hands at your next performance review meeting with your supervisor. Report back how that works out.*

- *Who says family holiday dinners are divisive? There are unexpected treasures hidden in gravy and mashed potatoes.*

- *Gravy (For My Mashed Potatoes) is a hit song filled with sexual longing. You can read the lyrics here: https://genius.com/Dee-dee-sharp-gravy-for-my-mashed-potatoes-lyrics and should probably avoid singing this at family gatherings.*

A Date

Full disclosure without removing your clothes

R. L. and Bethany sat in a booth at *Mangiano's Trattoria* looking at the street scene, including the subway entrance.

"I love to watch the people, think about their lives, observe their behaviors. Everyone seems so rushed, they scurry about, usually with their heads down. No one even seems to be paying attention." R. L. pointed to several pedestrians to illustrate.

She nodded. "I agree for the most part. They look kinda beat up and worn down and in a hurry to get somewhere. Home probably––it's end of the day and the week." Bethany continued, "And, you're right about the people watching thing. Like Yogi Berra said,

"'You can observe a lot by watching.'" They said it together and laughed.

"My favorite quote from him…" He scanned the small, but packed restaurant and gestured, "Nobody goes there anymore because it's too crowded." At that moment, a hand shot up and began to wave. A couple approached.

"Blythe, Ant Man? I almost don't recognize you guys, why are you so dressed up?"

"We just finished meeting with the Congressman." Blythe spoke.

"Are you kidding? You're not thinking of going mainstream are you?"

"Never. But we do need to work with the current system until we can tear it all down to build something new. Are you going to introduce us?"

"Sorry. Blythe, Ant Man, this is Bethany. Bethany these are friends of mine. They're anarchists and activists."

"We prefer ultra-Libertarians. I'm Tony, the Ant is short for anti."

"Looks like R. L. has some interesting friends; nice to meet you. Plenty of room at our table, we haven't even ordered yet." Bethany slid over to make room.

Blythe answered, "Thanks, we have and it's takeout, maybe some other time. We've got an organizer meeting later. We'll sit with you for a few minutes. Besides, we don't want to barge in on your dinner."

"What's the meeting about?" Bethany asked.

"Tonight we're working on getting the Occupy Wall Street movement up and running again, but we're involved in a lot of different rallies and protests." Tony rattled off a litany of issues: government corruption, racial injustice, climate change, privacy rights, policing reform, GMO labeling, healthcare for all, and half-dozen other activist concerns.

"Well, if you organize anything for animal rights or literacy, let me know. Those are two causes I'm passionate about."

"Those aren't so popular these days," Blythe responded. "Would you like to lead a team? How do we get in touch with you? Through R. L.? Maybe you can drag him along, but I doubt it." She turned to R. L. "What's the story with you guys--you a couple, friends, friends with bene-fits?"

"Slow down, please." R. L. addressed Bethany, "Blythe gets a little carried away." He turned to Blythe. "We haven't figured that out yet. It's our first date."

Just then an overhead announcement pro-claimed, "Ant Man, takeout for Ant Man. Your order is ready."

Tony smiled, "That's us. Have fun you two."

Blythe looked at Bethany and added, "R. L. 's really sweet, if you like nihilism, he's a poster child." They left.

"Hey, Arl..." she laughed, "your friends are in-teresting for sure. There's a lot to unpack there."

R. L. grabbed a menu. "Let's order first and then slow meal with lots of time for questions, answers, and discussion. How does that work for you?"

"Deal."

The food was great and same for the conversation which never lagged. They shared backgrounds. They talked about the books Bethany had recommended and a host of others. Bethany laughed when R. L. told her the story of how he got his name. She shared some funny stories of her own.

"So, let me get this straight, you're saying the boss left you in charge when he left? The office must have devolved into chaos without all the micromanagement. What happened?"

The waiter refilled their wine glasses. "That's the funny thing. First off Monday morning I told everybody I planned to leave them alone and trusted they would do a bang-up job, but if they didn't that was fine too. I told them not to bother me unless they couldn't figure it out on their own."

"Did they?"

"Bother me, no. Figure out whatever they needed to, absolutely. Other than running out of toilet paper in the men's restroom, nothing happened. The female staff were sporting enough to donate a roll. They all bought me lunch today, said it had been the most relaxed week ever. Stats for the week looked great, but I take no credit. They did all the work, I just got out the way."

"What do you think your boss will say when he gets back?"

R. L. shrugged, "Probably ask me to write a report. I don't know and can't say that I especially care. If he does ask for a report, I'll just figure out how to say I told everyone I didn't care what happened and this is what happened."

"Might need to express that a little more tactfully." Bethany grinned at the apparent contradiction of how not caring produced better results. "Maybe something along the lines of 'less is more'."

They covered a variety of other topics. At first, she thought it hilarious that Tony's aspiration in life was to be assassinated. His explanation rested upon the belief that only important people wind up getting assassinated.

"Really, that is over the top! Imagine the headline: 'Ant Man Assassinated!'" Then she grew more serious. "I do admire that level of passion and commitment. You have to admit the world is pretty messed up."

That launched lengthy discussion about politics, religion, social ills, and a host of heated topics that they sometimes agreed about and often did not. Bethany certainly did not shy away from expressing her strong opinions. She seemed to return time and again to his position of not thinking that so many of the many things they discussed represented anything to get worked up about.

"As I see it, people get their hair on fire about trivial things like professional sports, Twitter posts, fashion *faux paus*, kneeling or not kneeling, who is airing the best TV and commercials, or any other of dozens of pretty trivial things that don't matter much. As I see it..."

R. L. paused mid-sentence and pointed to a man at the top of the subway stairs. "I recognize that guy." Through the glass, he and the Walker made eye contact, they both thrust out their chins and mouthed,

"Hey."

The Walker motioned with both arms as though jogging in place and spoke. Though silent through the window, the words were clear: "Gotta keep movin'."

R. L. shared the subway connection story with Bethany. "You see, that's the kind of stuff I find meaningful. We are two strangers connected in the web of humanity in some intangible way."

"Granted, and I see your point. It's way more meaningful than what type of deodorant an Instagram influencer is touting, that's for sure. But *carte blanche* nihilism? That sounds like disinterest and withdrawal. You can't deny there are big problems in the world and if you are not part of the solution, you are most definitely part of the problem."

"That's not the sort of nihilism I'm talking about. Not caring in a self-centered, selfish, it doesn't affect me so why should I care kind of way, isn't what I'm suggesting. I'm saying not to get distracted by the trivial b.s., all the silly nonsense things like brand of deodorant you just mentioned and everything a bunch of corporate and media gurus think you want to know about the secrets of the Royal Family. I can continue with more if you want the full infomercial version."

"Go on, I'm listening, but the condensed version is fine. Endless drivel about the Monarchy covers the entire mindset of filling in a vacuous void with voluminous valueless vapidity. It's a *tabula rasa* filled by a tabloid treasure trove of worthless rubbish."

"Wow, I couldn't have captured that so succinctly. It's astounding that people want to fill the void that way; they crave to consume such drivel. You could argue that's a different version of nihilism, a rejection of the meaningful and embrace of the meaningless."

Bethany continued. "We agree on that, but what about the big stuff? The stuff Blythe and Tony are working on, big social justice issues and inequalities? If everyone is passive and can't be bothered, we won't have much of a world or a society worth living in."

"I agree. Where I disagree is how to change it for the betterment of all. It's not an approach my two dear friends would agree with."

"So, what is your approach? You must care about something. If it's not the big things and it's certainly not the trivial things, what do you care about, Rectum Leviticus?" She folded her hands and invited his explanation. "What exactly is your philosophy, your brand of nihilism?"

"Quite simple really. I have four things on my list of things that I care about. And, quite honestly, I care deeply about. I used to have more, but I've narrowed it down to four.

Bethany leaned forward and seemed to hold her breath.

"One––Mephisto. But the gecko represents relationships in general. There are some relationships that require time and effort and cultivating, and they are worth caring about. At the moment, Mephisto is alone in that category and he or she is presently MIA."

She sighed. "Okay, that makes sense and hopefully that category will expand. What's next?"

She blinked and for a moment, it reminded R. L. of the same sort of blink as Mephisto's.

"Next is the library and what it represents. Shared knowledge, experience, wisdom, insights, all free for public consumption––I don't think I need to explain that further."

As Bethany nodded, R. L. continued. "Third is respect. I value respect and treasure it. If more people simply respected one another, including differences of opinion, many of the big things on the list of social problems would improve mightily."

As staff cleared the table, Bethany used the restroom after claiming she couldn't hold on for the final item on his list. When she returned and settled back in, they sipped coffee.

"Okay, R. L., the suspense is killing me. So far, I like your list. Did you save the best for last or is last the least?

"You decide for yourself. I think it's the most important and it's so simple really. Try to make the world a better place. I try and do my part to make the world incrementally a teeny-tiny bit better. I know that's a bit subjective and my value judgment about better and worse might be different from someone else's, but if collectively we just each did a small part the impact would be huge. Don't you agree?"

"Makes sense. Be the change you seek. Buddhist in a way."

"Actually, the Buddha was a nihilist."

"I didn't know that." Her cellphone chimed. "That's the shelter... Just before closing...wonder what they want?" Bethany read a text and her eyes grew wide. She summarized the message. "The Jane Goodall Shelter––they're downtown––called our shelter looking for me. I had been in touch with them previously asking about any geckos that might have been turned in. Someone left a gecko there today. Recognize this fella?"

She slid her phone over displaying an image of a smiling lizard's face.

R. L. cocked his head first to the right, then to the left. He squinted. "Hard to say for sure, but it could be Mephisto. That would be so utterly awesome if it is. Are they open tomorrow? I'll be there first thing in the morning. Can you text them?Bethany obliged with quick thumb strokes. R. L. tried to restrain himself from false hope but when she finished, he couldn't hold back from clasping Bethany's hands.

Tears welled. "Thank you! Thank you so much!"

A Cheshire-cat grin lit her face. "And there I was thinking you don't care about things. Something strange about you R. L.––you're more caring than most. The sensitive and caring nihilist is more appealing than the 'I don't give a shit about anything' kind."

"Bethany, you don't mince words, that's for sure." He rolled up his sleeve and pointed to his FYN tattoo but didn't tell her the meaning and misdirection from the choice of font. He would save that story for a different day. "This has been a lot of FUN!"

***

Mephisto perched on the coffee table and crunched away. If the lizard had stories to tell, R. L. would never learn them. What little he found out had to do with a steam pipe in a building next door. His buddy had apparently been lost close by but worlds away in urban disconnection. He watched the lizard, and recognized the contentment of home, warmth, and a full belly. Sunlight reflected a moment from his new used toaster. It looked the same as his old one and very well could have been reclaimed by the original owner post theft and $7.00, and now returned to its rightful place on the countertop. He laughed—*life is good!*

A text message stirred him from his reverie. He laughed some more. Vanessa inviting him to the next book club meeting represented all sorts of possibilities. Dolfe had returned to Denmark claiming America was just too crazy and messed up for him. A universe of possibilities unfolded with infinite potential.

"You know something, Mephisto?" The gecko ignored him. "I'll tell you little buddy, the world is pretty crazy but the universe is crazy funny, a big cosmic joke."

If it's possible for geckos to lengthen their smiles, R. L. swore that's what happened, and then Mephisto winked.

If you want to join R. L. and wink back, read on:

Rectum's Survival Tips, Part Fourteen:

- *Stop LOLing by cute texting and funny faced emojis and actually laugh out loud. There are countless funny things to laugh about. Look in the mirror and start with yourself. Make a goofy face. See, that wasn't hard.*

- *House geckos make good companions and pets. They are excellent listeners and less expensive than therapists.*

- *If you feel your life lacks meaning and purpose, you might be absolutely right. Don't give up; give in. Give in to the (fill in* _the blank space here with your name) what is really meaningful to me foundation. Donate your time and energy generously. If you still lack meaning and purpose, at least you will be generously resourced._

- _The universe is filled with comic and cosmic humor and so should you be. Start a narrative that begins with: You and a nihilist meet for the first time and are just getting acquainted in an effort to compare survival tactics and strategies. What happens next...?_

***

The Nihilist lives on and continues to share his wit and wisdom on Facebook and Instagram.

Rectum's Remarks:

https://www.facebook.com/profile.php?id =61555713576084

rl_the_nihilist:

https://www.instagram.com/rl_the_nihilist/

Acknowledgements

I want to thank my family, friends, critique group members, and my editor. All of their names are withheld to protect the innocent.

My further thanks to all readers of this handbook. Hopefully you have not depleted your supply of mind-altering substances and/or painkillers to make it all the way to the end.

I am grateful for your support!

About the Author

Tungyn Cheque prefers to remain anonymous. Know that he is always on the lookout for the absurd and farcical everyday situations that other people miss. He appreciates that humor is all around us, and that modern society provides an abundance of things to not take so seriously. He has learned to watch, smile, be fascinated by, and contemplate new survival tactics.

Mr. Cheque is a distinguished graduate of Flâneur University, and matriculated with honors from The Royal Academy of Studious Humans. He is enrolled in continuing education at the Institute for the Advancement of Nonsense. Tungyn Cheque is a member of the American Society of Subversives and the League of Laughter.

***

Tungyn Cheque is an alias for Victor Acquista, an international award-winning author of serious fiction and nonfiction. Learn more here: https://victoracquista.com/ or visit his Amazon Author page.

Milton Keynes UK
Ingram Content Group UK Ltd.
UKHW030659120324
439302UK00015B/786